D1133242

NAGASAKI: The Forgotten Bomb

NAGASAKI: The Forgotten Bomb

Frank W. Chinnock

AN NAL BOOK
THE WORLD PUBLISHING COMPANY
New York and Cleveland

FIRST PRINTING
PUBLISHED BY THE NEW AMERICAN LIBRARY, INC.
IN ASSOCIATION WITH
THE WORLD PUBLISHING COMPANY
2231 WEST 110TH STREET
CLEVELAND, OHIO 44102

LIBRARY OF CONGRESS CATALOG CARD NUMBER: 68-9779
PRINTED IN THE UNITED STATES OF AMERICA

This book is dedicated to all
the people who were there that day

"A Time when Hell itself breeds out
Contagion to this world . . ."

Hamlet, William Shakespeare

Preface

IT COULD HAVE BEEN A FRENCH CITY, OR A SPANISH ONE. IT could have taken place in Australia, or in South America, or in Laos. It could have been a Russian city—or an American one. The fact that an atomic bomb exploded over a city called Nagasaki in Japan is almost incidental—except to those who were there. It could have happened elsewhere. It still can.

This is a testimony of those who went through it, who remember. Two bombs, two very special bombs, have been dropped on people in our lifetime. The first, at Hiroshima, has been the subject of books, articles, movies, editorials, crusades. The Nagasaki bomb, anticlimactic as it must have seemed, has been ignored by the world, virtually forgotten. Yet thousands of people, mostly civilians, died in that second special holocaust—the Americans estimate 40,000, the Japanese twice that figure. The exact number is not the important fact. What matters is how the individual felt and reacted, how he survived, or did not survive.

Many of the survivors can now talk about that day in

August, 1945. By written word, or voice, or via relatives, they have contributed over 2,000 experiences to this story. Some of the survivors, persecuted by superstitious countrymen, ignored by their own government, deprived of jobs, with their sons and daughters unable to marry because prospective mates believe they or their children may inherit the dread A-bomb "disease," have gone underground and revealed their personal histories only with the author's promise of anonymity. For that reason some of the names have been changed.

But what is here written is not fiction. It happened. Much as the survivors remember, or try to forget, that day, it is now so recorded.

Acknowledgments

WHEN I FIRST STARTED THE RESEARCH ON THIS BOOK, MANY people warned me of the difficulties involved: the hostility of the survivors, the problem of working in a foreign language, the high cost and length of time necessary to complete the research, the difficulty of locating the pilot and crew of the plane, and the staggering job of assembling the bits and pieces into a readable book. But those predictions were either wrong or were overcome by the generosity and efforts of other people.

In Japan, the survivors were rarely hostile, but almost always cooperative and friendly. To cope with the problems of language and cost, I was most fortunate in having the backing of The Reader's Digest of Japan, Ltd. In particular, I would like to thank Mr. Iwao Nakamura of that staff for his tireless and meticulous help in interviewing people in Nagasaki. His contribution was of incalculable value.

So many people helped: John Taylor at the National Archives; Miss Anna Urband at the Book and Magazine Section of the Department of Defense; Mr. Ikematsu, former director of the Nagasaki Cultural Hall; General Sweeney, Admiral Ashworth, and the crew of that special B-29; Marylou Meese; Yoko Matsumura; and Akiko Sugawara, herself an author, for her special counsel. At The New American Library, I am indebted to Robert Gutwillig for his advice and encouragement, to Barbara Collins for her infallible pencil, and to all of the many people there who were responsible for bringing out a book anyone could be proud of.

Finally, I would like to thank my wife, Jan, who, during those difficult eighteen months, had to live with me, bear with me, offer constant praise, and listen, and listen, and listen.

Contents

PROLOGUE

NAGASAKI TODAY IS A CITY ALIVE, THROBBING AND AS HAPPY AS it can be with the memories and scars of its time of pain. It died once, a hard remembrance to erase. Still, the people of this southern Japanese city do not dwell overmuch on the past. Unlike their counterparts at Hiroshima, who seem to have clasped their own particular agony to their bosoms, the people here are somewhat like a sturdy peasant housewife who over the years has given birth to seven children—three of them stillborn. She can live her life in sorrow, remembering her three dead infants. Instead, she has nodded her head in resignation. So be it! Life must go on, after all, and there are still four healthy children to rear and send on their way. Forget the past and look ahead! The scars may still be there, but they are well hidden and stoically accepted in this most Catholic of all Japanese cities.

In shape, the city is like a two-tined fork with mountainous ridges between the tines and to the outside of them. Nagasaki —the name means "long valley"—is actually two parallel valleys, one long, one short. The heel of the fork and the shorter right-hand valley comprise the downtown section and the old city. The left-hand valley is called the Urakami Valley. Some residents who have lived there for years refer to it as "the Valley of the Shadows of Death."

Nagasaki is still a city small enough to walk through, and in the spring, with the delicate cherry blossoms in bloom, it can be a memorable stroll. If you start walking directly away from the harbor to the northwest along the left valley, you go along Urakami Avenue, a wide concrete street laid over the old cobblestones and split by streetcar tracks. Parallel to the road on your left is the narrow Urakami River, once a favorite swimming spot for youngsters.

Should you decide to cross the main avenue, you must do so with great care, for the traffic is heavy and fast. In that hot summer of 1945, however, there were no taxis or private cars, and the buses burned wood for fuel. There were no motor bikes, no trucks, and only a few military vehicles. The streets, except for bicycles and people, were almost empty. There was no automotive transport for a simple reason: There was virtually no gasoline. A saying, widely circulated at the time, summed it up: "A drop of gasoline equals a drop of blood."

The people of Nagasaki eat well today. But during that fateful August, there was no meat, no pastry, no cameras, for taking pictures was forbidden. There were no eggs, no milk, no coffee and very little tea. There was some fish and a quarter of a normal ration of rice, and what vegetables there were had to be coaxed out of small backyard plots or doled out of larger communal ones. Substitute "coffee" was made by roasting soybeans, and one had to be an addict indeed to swallow the bitter mixture which could not even be improved by the addition of sugar because there was none of that either. One also had to be somewhat of an addict to smoke in those days, for aside from illegal or privileged sources, tobacco was nonexistent. Substitutes were numerous and imaginative—but always unsatisfactory. The most common was chopped grass or hay in a tissue-thin page of an English dictionary.

About two miles from the harbor, in the middle of the Valley of the Shadows of Death, you come to a road that curves sharply up a hill to your right. At the top is a light-gray, blocklike building, made of stones imported from a nearby island, which stands about a hundred feet high. Called the Nagasaki Cultural Center, it was built in 1955 as a monument to an unforgettable day ten years earlier. Facing west from the Cultural Center and down seventy-six tilted concrete steps is a small memorial park lined with Japanese cedars, a few pines and plantings of various kinds. Old women with white kerchiefs over their heads, dressed in bulky sweaters, black *mompei* (baggy slacks) and white sneakers, work throughout each day, picking up twigs, debris and weeds to keep the little park attractive. In the center of it lies a rectangular plot of sickly green-brown grass, about forty by eighty feet, surrounded by gravel paths. Two lion-like gargoyles guard the sides, snarling soundlessly at awestruck visitors. Despite the meticulous efforts to keep the park tended and lovely, it is, somehow, a gloomy place, a depressing spot. It symbolizes the epicenter of the second atomic bomb.

You stand in the middle of that rectangular plot and gaze upward, squinting into the bright spring sun, the clear innocent sky, and for some reason you begin to shiver. It is almost impossible to conceive of the fact that not so very long ago, some five hundred yards directly over where you are now standing, the sky burst apart and a city died. Now it is alive once more, but that is a rebirth, what the Buddhists here call "reincarnation," or another chance at life. The fact remains that the city died once, a painful, violent, sad death. And it happened right over this spot. . . .

SUMMER, 1945

CHAPTER 1

Special Mission No. 16

0256 HOURS

IN THE EARLY MORNING BLACKNESS OF THAT AUGUST 9TH, A genial, exuberant 25-year-old Irishman named Charles Sweeney, Major, U. S. Army Air Force, was running out of runway on an island called Tinian in the Pacific Ocean. He was not genial at the moment, for on board was an atomic bomb, the greatest instrument of destruction ever devised by man. Three days before, when he and his crew on the instrument plane had flown with Colonel Paul Tibbets on the epic Hiroshima mission, his plane had been considerably lighter and it had been a routine takeoff. But this time, there was an extra 10,000 pounds aboard—five tons of destruction—and as the ocean rushed toward him at the end of the two-mile-long runway, Sweeney wondered whether he would be able to lift the heavy B-29 in time.

Others on the ground, watching, were wondering the same thing, and with much more trepidation than they had felt watching the *Enola Gay* strain at her takeoff on her flight to

Hiroshima. For there was a vast difference between the two missions and the two bombs: Photographers and high brass had been on hand for the lift-off of the historic *first* "A-bomb" mission. At the outset of this mission, however, there were no lights, no photographers, no fanfare. The second atomic drop was being left to the professionals. Furthermore, the core of the bomb dropped from the *Enola Gay* was uranium, and the bomb had been final-armed during the flight. But the core of the atomic bomb on Sweeney's plane was plutonium, and it was already in place. If the plane crashed, the detonators might explode and trigger a nuclear reaction. If that happened, not only the plane, but much of the island of Tinian would be just a memory.

For some reason, the lights at the end of the runway had been turned off that morning. So the others never knew just how close the B-29 came to the warm waters of the Pacific. But Chuck Sweeney knew, and he let out his breath in relief as he felt the wheels leave the ground and the propellers bite the air and the wind begin to lift the silver wings up into the dark sky. They were airborne.

"Wheels up!" Sweeney ordered, and Copilot Don Albury hit the switch. "Flaps up! Give me power two," he added, calling for climbing power to 2,400 rpm.

Slowly, the four Curtis Wright Cyclone engines took the big bird up to 7,000 feet, above the clouds. At an air speed of 220 miles an hour, Sweeney headed north along the course that Navigator Jimmy Van Pelt had given him. Actually, Van Pelt's job had just begun. Right now, he was busy checking the airplane compass with his navigator's astro-compass, computing true air speed, taking drift readings, and, along with Radarman Ed Buckley, taking radar bearings from the various available beacons. Throughout the flight he would be doing these things constantly, as well as taking celestial fixes and giving position reports to Radioman Abe Spitzer just in case they got in trouble and had to ditch. That possibility made him grimace whenever he thought about it. Imagine having to ditch with "the Gimmick" still on board!

For Sweeney, this was the easy part of the job. There was little for him to do other than drive the ship. He knew that the crew could handle its tasks without any interference from him; the men had had intensive training and had been thoroughly briefed for this mission. After supper the officers in the crew, Sweeney, Don Albury, Third Pilot Fred Olivi, Van Pelt and Bombardier Kermit Beahan, had studied endless maps of the two Japanese cities they were expected to recognize better than their own home towns: Kokura and Nagasaki. The aiming points of each—the Kokura arsenal and the Mitsubishi Shipyards in the harbor of Nagasaki—were firmly imprinted in their minds.

They also knew what to expect. Both the officers and the enlisted men, Buckley, Spitzer, Dehart, Kuharek and Gallagher, had already been shown films of the test A-bomb explosion at Alamogordo. They all knew that they were carrying a duplicate of that same bomb.

On the evening of August 8, at an area of the field where "the Shed" was located, three scientists had discussed the possible effects of the plutonium bomb and how they could make a further contribution to the mission. It had been hoped that the Hiroshima bomb would prompt Japan to surrender at once, but there had been no indication of any forthcoming surrender. Perhaps the Japanese leaders had not grasped the enormity of the atomic threat to their nation. One of the scientists, Dr. Luis Alvarez, remembered that a Japanese physicist, Professor Sagane, had studied with them at the University of California in 1938. Dr. Alvarez and his colleagues decided that, if anyone could, Sagane would be able to explain the destructive force of the new weapon to the Japanese military leaders and convince them of the folly of continued resistance. So Alvarez wrote a message to his former colleague, pleading with him to seek peace. Later, this was taped to the inside of the instrument capsule that Captain Fred Bock in the second plane would drop over the target.

At about 11:00 P.M. on the eighth, the crews of three planes assembled in a large, closely-guarded Quonset hut for the final briefing. Colonel Paul Tibbets, commander of the top-secret 509th Composite Group and the pilot of the *Enola Gay,* was the first to address the group. He told them that *their* atomic bomb, called "Fat Man" for its distinctive Churchillian shape, differed from the "Little Boy" dropped on Hiroshima and was more powerful; and that he had been assured that scientists could now produce bombs like Fat Man swiftly and in quantity. For that reason, all eyes in Washington were now focused on them. He spoke to all present, but his words must have been especially impressive to Major Charles Sweeney and nine of the thirteen members of the strike plane crew. These men, unique in history, were the only ten Americans who could later claim to have witnessed at first hand the explosions of the only two atomic bombs ever dropped on people.

The intelligence experts took over from there. The mission, the men were informed, was called simply "Special Bombing Mission No. 16." Three pilots in three different planes would be involved—Major Chuck Sweeney, Captain Fred Bock and Major Jim Hopkins. Sweeney's regular plane, *The Great Artiste,* named by the crew in honor of Beahan's technique with a bombsight and with the opposite sex, had already been outfitted with special instruments and used on the Hiroshima flight. Because of this, it was decided that Sweeney would use Bock's plane, fittingly named *Bock's Car,* as the strike plane, and have Captain Fred Bock fly *The Great Artiste* as the instrument plane. Major Jim Hopkins would fly the third plane which would carry movie cameras and scientific personnel, including Group Captain Leonard

Chesire, Winston Churchill's official representative. On Sweeney's plane, three additional personnel complemented his usual ten men: Lieutenant Commander Frederick L. Ashworth, the "weaponeer" in charge of the bomb, his assistant, Lieutenant Phil Barnes, and the radar countermeasures specialist, Lieutenant Jake Beser, whose job it was to make sure that the Japanese did not electronically detonate Fat Man ahead of schedule. Captain Bock in the second plane would also have an extra passenger: journalist William L. Laurence of *The New York Times* who had been chosen to cover the Mahattan Project from its inception to its conclusion and whose coverage of the entire event would win him a Pulitzer Prize.

In that final briefing, every possible contingency was covered—altitude, navigation, weather, rescue, special instructions. The three planes would fly at 7,000 feet, climb to a bombing altitude of 31,000 and rendezvous at Yakashima, a small island off the coast of southern Kyushu. There, two weather planes sent out hours earlier would report the weather conditions over both targets, Kokura and Nagasaki. From the beginning, radio silence would be absolute. There was no way of ascertaining whether the Japanese had learned the lesson of Hiroshima and would be waiting for a similar small formation to appear over the home islands. In case any of the planes had to ditch, the airmen were informed, there would be rescue ships at such-and-such positions and waiting aircraft to pinpoint the downed plane. There was even a substitute B-29 at Iwo Jima ready and waiting in case anything went wrong on the way. Both Sweeney and Ashworth were told in no uncertain terms that the bomb *must* be dropped by visual, nonradar sighting of the aiming point. It was a case of "naked eye or scratch."

The meeting ended when Chaplain Downey prayed for the men going into battle. "Almighty God, Father of all mercies, we pray Thee to be gracious with those who fly this night. Guard and protect those of us who venture out into the darkness of Thy heaven. Uphold them on Thy wings. Keep them safe both in body and soul and bring them back to us. Give to us all courage and strength for the hours that are ahead; give to them rewards according to their efforts. Above all else, our Father, bring peace to Thy world. May we go forward trusting in Thee and knowing we are in Thy presence now and forever. Amen."

Shortly afterward, at about 2:00 A.M., Sweeney and the crew strolled out to the hardstand and stood around chatting about the night, the weather, home, girls—just about anything except the upcoming mission. They were solemn, and at the same time keyed up, even though some had gone through it a mere three days earlier. But there was a big difference. This time *they* would be carrying the ball.

Sweeney's senses seemed acute that night. He was attuned to sight and sound to an unusual degree. Just to the right of the hangars, he noticed that "the Shed" was now in darkness, the hum of its air-conditioners silent. That had been Fat Man's home, an air-cooled, super-secret, dust-free, lint-free, mysterious place in which the last delicate mechanism of Fat Man's guts had been assembled. It was empty and deserted now, with no cordon of guards around it. Fat Man had found a new home—in the underbelly of *Bock's Car.* Sweeney and Ashworth were its new masters.

Just before "start-engine" time. Sweeney called together his flight crew and, standing alongside of the plane, said to them: "This is what we have been working for, testing and thinking about for the past year. You were with me on the Hiroshima mission. As you know, that was executed perfectly, flown beautifully and dropped on the button. I want our mission to be exactly the same—executed just as perfectly. Remember, it must be executed at all costs. We *will* get the bomb on target, even if we go down with it."

The men responded as he had known they would—not with empty-courage words, but with a quiet determination written on each face. There was no need for bravado. The crew had been together almost since the activation of Operation Centerboard, the code name for the "implementation of the bomb in combat." On Tinian they had endured criticism and jeers from the other fliers, who had been losing as much as 15 percent of their planes every day. Just who the hell were these "untouchables" anyhow, these "glory boys who were going to win the war all by themselves"? Unable to explain or talk back because of the secrecy of their mission, Sweeney's men had turned to each other for companionship, and had thus become even more close-knit than usual wartime comrades. They had trained for almost a year, at remote Wendover Field in Utah, at Batista Field in Cuba, and at the coral island of Tinian. Now they knew each other almost as they knew themselves. Sweeney was sure that they all realized, as did he, that this was the culmination of all their preparation. Today was what they had been training for —to end the war with honor and go back to the business of living.

As the crew stood on the hardstand wanting nothing more than to get going, a major problem arose. The flight engineer, Sergeant John Kuharek, after the preflight check, walked over to Sweeney and said, "Skipper, we got troubles. An auxiliary transfer fuel pump is out of whack. That means that our reserve fuel is trapped in one of the bomb-bay tanks."

Colonel Tibbets, somehow sensing trouble, approached Sweeney, his pipe stuck firmly in his mouth, his eyebrows raised questioningly. Sweeney explained the situation and the two men discussed alternatives. To abort the mission at this point might mean a delay of several days, perhaps a week. This second drop had originally been scheduled for August 11, but had been moved ahead two days when the weather boys had predicted a general socking-in of weather, including a typhoon moving up from Iwo to Japan. Both men realized the importance of delivering a quick one-two punch against the Empire, that this dual blow could drastically shorten the war. But in the end, Tibbets left the decision to Sweeney.

It was typical of the Old Man, Sweeney thought. Once Paul Tibbets placed his trust in a man, it was there permanently, not to be withdrawn on a whim. That was one of the main reasons why Chuck Sweeney was so torn by the choice facing him now. Five days earlier, he had been proud and honored when Tibbets had said that he wanted him, Chuck, to lead the second mission. Now he wanted desperately to live up to Tibbets' faith in him. He couldn't let the Old Man down with a bad performance, and with no reserve fuel there would be little margin for error.

He saw that his men were watching him, waiting for the decision that would affect them all. Sweeney took a deep breath, and made up his mind. "The hell with it," he said with an unaccustomed touch of anger. "We're going anyway." He had suddenly remembered that the plane could always stop off at Okinawa or Iwo Jima on the return trip and refuel. The men nodded and walked away slowly.

Colonel Tibbets also nodded in agreement, and Sweeney smiled. He remembered an incident that had taken place earlier that evening and told Tibbets about it. An admiral had taken Sweeney aside and said, "Young man, do you know how much the bomb in your plane cost the United States Government?"

"No, sir," Sweeney had answered respectfully.

The admiral had squinted at him and waved a finger under his nose. "That bomb, and all the work that went into it, cost in the neighborhood of two billion dollars," he had said. "Now, tell me, do you know how much your airplane cost?"

Sweeney, who had been associated with the early testing of B-29s, knew to the dollar. "Yes, Admiral," he had replied. "A little over a half a million dollars."

The admiral had peered at him, nodded, and said, "Young man, just bear that in mind."

Sweeney laughed when he related the story to Tibbets. "I got the message all right: Never mind what happens to us and the plane. Just get that bomb to the target!"

Tibbets had smiled in appreciation and looked long at Sweeney. "There's no reason why men and machine can't both function successfully," he had said.

0400 HOURS

AN HOUR AFTER TAKEOFF ON THE NINTH, *Bock's Car* WAS cruising steadily at 7,000 feet. Half a mile behind Sweeney's plane, reporter Bill Laurence sat in the midsection of *The Great Artiste* alternately staring out of the window into the darkness and taking notes. Laurence had been bitterly disappointed at being left off the Hiroshima mission, but there had been no room for him then. Now, on this second mission, he was at last to witness the results of the four years of monumental effort. He turned a page in his notebook and wrote: "Somewhere ahead of me lies Japan, the land of our enemy. In a few hours from now, one of its cities, making weapons of war for use against us, will be wiped off the map by the greatest weapon ever made by man. In a fraction of time immeasurable by any clock, a whirlwind from the skies will pulverize thousands of its buildings and tens of thousands of its inhabitants. Does one feel any pity or compassion for the poor devils about to die? Not when one thinks of Pearl Harbor and of the Death March on Bataan."

Up ahead Sweeney's plane was plowing through a small storm, dipping and sloughing in the turbulence. Lieutenant Commander Ashworth carefully watched the "black box," the monitor of the bomb's innards, to make sure nothing was amiss. The storm was soon over and Sweeney turned to his copilot, Don Albury. "So far, so good." He smiled his genial Irish smile.

But Albury seemed worried. "That trapped gas may be a headache."

Sweeney shrugged. "Why cross bridges?"

A minute later he said to Albury, "Want to take her for awhile?"

"Sure. It's an easy ride." Albury's hands gripped the wheel and began to drive the plane.

Sweeney swiveled around in his seat and looked backward. Fred Olivi was asleep in the seat behind him, and beyond, squatting in front of the ominous black box were Ashworth and his assistant, Lieutenant Barnes. In the rear compartment, Sergeant Spitzer was reading a *Reader's Digest* condensation of *Our Hearts Were Young and Gay*. Flight Engineer Kuharek, looking worried, had his eyes glued to the fuel gauges and the other instruments which helped him compute their rate of consumption.

Beahan, a great "sack" man, was asleep as usual. Albury had told Sweeney how he had once had to wake Beahan at 3:00 A.M. and Beahan had said in a sleepy Texas drawl: "A great artiste like me doesn't have to get up this early. He lets the other boys take care of that." The nickname had stuck and had been a unanimous choice for the name of their plane.

Sweeney now saw no reason why he shouldn't steal a page from Beahan's book. He lifted his 200 pounds out of the seat, crawled back into the rear of the compartment, and lay down. He had had very little rest in the last three days, and he figured that this was going to be a long flight. He lay there in the darkness for a few minutes wondering how his wife Dorothy, in Boston, Massachusetts, would feel when she heard the name of the pilot who had dropped the second atomic bomb. Then the need for sleep became too great to resist.

The people in Nagasaki were also asleep for the most part, and the war-darkened city was almost invisible as it hugged the mountains that surrounded it.

CHAPTER 2

The City Awakens

From the diary of Professor Raisuke Shirabe of the Nagasaki Medical College:

ON THE MORNING OF AUGUST 9, A REALLY FINE MORNING, I AROSE FROM MY BED IN MY OFFICE AT THE UNIVERSITY HOSPITAL AT SIX. AFTER LEISURELY WASHING AND BRUSHING MY TEETH, I WENT TO THE SECOND FLOOR WHERE I ATE BREAKFAST WITH OTHER PROFESSORS AT THE COLLEGE.

OUR TALK CENTERED AROUND THE GROWING AUSTERITY IN NAGASAKI. MY WIFE AND I, ONLY YESTERDAY, HAD GONE FAR OUT INTO THE COUNTRY TO FORAGE FOR FOOD FOR OUR LARGE FAMILY. EVEN NOW, MY FACE BURNS WITH SHAME AT THE MEMORY OF HAVING TO PLEAD WITH FARMERS TO SELL US SOME FOOD, WHICH I, A UNIVERSITY PROFESSOR, THEN HAD TO CARRY AWAY ON MY BACK, LIKE AN OX.

WE ALSO DISCUSSED UNIVERSITY PRESIDENT TSUNOO'S DESCRIPTION OF THE DAMAGE CAUSED BY THE "NEW-TYPE" BOMB USED AT HIROSHIMA. THAT EVENT HAD ONLY REAFFIRMED MY CONVICTION THAT THE WAR WAS NOW REACHING A CRITICAL STAGE, DESPITE THE PRESS REPORTS OF CONTINUING GLORIOUS VICTORIES. I AM GLAD THAT I DECIDED TO MOVE MY WIFE AND THE YOUNGER CHILDREN TO A RENTED ROOM IN A FARMHOUSE IN THE SUBURBS. ONLY MY TWO OLDEST SONS REMAIN WITH ME HERE AT THE MEDICAL COLLEGE THIS DAY.

THE AIR-RAID ALERT HAS JUST SOUNDED AND WE MUST SEEK SHELTER ONCE MORE. WILL IT NEVER END?

0400 HOURS

MRS. TAE ADACHI, AN ATTRACTIVE 29-YEAR-OLD TEACHER AT Yamazato Primary School, had slept fitfully that night, tossing and turning. Finally, she arose much earlier than usual and while her children and sister slept, she fixed herself a cup of tea and kneeled with *shoji* open looking at her tiny vegetable plot, watching the sun come up. But somehow, when that event took place, the very spectacle filled her with sadness, for it was no longer Japan's Rising Sun and the light it cast was now a sickly yellow one. Although she was convinced of her soldier-husband's death, she knew that she was not truly aware of the consequences of it. He had been away in the Imperial Army for such long periods during the past five years, the last one for over a year, that she had almost grown accustomed to his absence, to fashioning her life around the dual role of both mother and provider. But she was beginning to realize that when the war was over and other husbands returned, she would still be alone. There would be only the children left.

Long after sun-up, she heard one of her children cry out and, finishing her now-cold tea, she rose and went to check. But it was only a cry from the darkness of child sleep, and she started to fix something for breakfast. She relit the charcoal brazier to heat the leftover bean soup and, waiting, flipped on the radio, hoping to hear the latest news. While the coals heated, she fiddled with the dials, and all at once, an excited voice filled her ears: ". . . bomb was dropped on the city of Hiroshima at 8:15 on the morning of August 6 and killed many thousands of people who were literally disintegrated by a searing blast of incredible power. This destruction will continue unless the Japanese people surrender at once. We warn you to . . ."

Mrs. Adachi hastily spun the dial, realizing that she had inadvertently picked up a forbidden broadcast by the enemy radio. Soon music was coming out of the speaker and she began to prepare the meager meal, unwilling to let her thoughts dwell on that fearful news flash. Her sister joined her but Mrs. Adachi said nothing about it, and half an hour later they both listened to the "official" news. She concentrated on the flat voice of the announcer, waiting to see whether there would be any official mention of the event. Finally, toward the end of the broadcast, the announcer said, "A few days ago, a new-type bomb was dropped on Hiroshima City causing some damage. An investigation is now under way."

How strange, she thought. There was a great difference between the two statements. Could there possibly be any truth in that first flash? Many strange things were happening in Japan these days. She glanced at her younger sister, that proud, unflinching young woman. No, best not say anything now. She would mention it casually that evening to her neighbor, Mrs. Fukuoka, though she was sure she could predict the other's reaction. Mrs. Fukuoka, one of the 10,000 Catholics who made Nagasaki the center of Christianity in Japan, would probably cross herself automatically and glance out the window toward the Urakami Cathedral, a block away in the Shiroyama district. Mrs. Adachi had to admit that even she, a Buddhist, drew some reassurance from the sight of that imposing structure. It was so old, so enduring.

As she prepared the soup, the words of that first forbidden announcement reentered her head, unwanted but persistent . . . "thousands were literally disintegrated . . ." If that were indeed true, what terrible kind of new bomb could it be, what kind of bomb could have killed so many at one time? All at once she thought of the leaflets that had been dropped on the outskirts of Nagasaki the day before, warning the people to evacuate the city. Her son had brought one home to her and she had been astonished at the precise Japanese lettering, at the poetry of the threat: "Back in April, Nagasaki was all flowers. August in Nagasaki there will be flame showers."

Her neighbors had told her that local government officials and the military stationed there had scoffed at the "stupid propaganda," assuring everyone that it was simply "vicious American lies." But now she began to wonder. Had Hiroshima received similar warnings just before it had been destroyed? Could Nagasaki possibly be next on the list? In any case, what could she, a helpless woman, do about it?

At about 8:00 A.M., after her children had been fed and told to "mind their aunt," Mrs. Adachi walked to the Yamazato school grounds, to work with her teacher colleagues in the communal vegetable garden in back of the main building, as she had been doing for most of that summer. That day, the teachers were divided into two groups—shelter diggers and vegetable tenders—and they started work in the sweltering heat. Soon she was hot, sweaty and more tired than she had been in a long time. If only this dreadful war could be ended, she thought. But she doubted it. The military leaders would never give up. She felt a breeze suddenly. It was most welcome.

0530 HOURS

IN *Bock's Car,* CHUCK SWEENEY HAD JUST TAKEN OVER AGAIN. Fred Olivi, the regular copilot when Sweeney did not fly, had relieved Albury and had been flying the plane for the last hour. Sweeney soon saw that everything was under control.

"Any problems?" he asked Olivi.

"A little turbulence. Nothing to worry about."

In the rear of the plane, Lieutenant Jake Beser, from

Baltimore, Maryland, was studying the special screen which monitored Japanese radio signals visually. Beside it was Beser's own little "black box" which later would set off the electronic proximity fuses within the bomb. At a precise moment, initiated by the bomb leaving the plane, a count-down would start. Beser's "black box" would begin sending radio signals down to earth which would bounce back to the falling bomb. The nineteenth bounce would activate the fuses.

Beser had been a "ham" radio operator since he was 11 years old. He had been a senior engineering student at Johns Hopkins University when war broke out, and he had been sent directly to radar school and applied tactics training by the Army Air Force. This was his fourteenth mission and he was the only man to fly in the *strike* plane of both atomic missions. Right now, he was engrossed in the second part of his job—to make certain that no Japanese radio or radar transmissions were on a close enough wavelength to cause premature detonation. He stared at the panoramic adapter in front of him, looking for sharp pulses on a wavelength near that which had been built into the fuses of the bomb. But there were no signals in the adjoining bands. Nothing was coming in.

Not far from Beser, Radioman Abe Spitzer had taken off his headphones and was watching the sun come up. Spitzer, a New Yorker born and bred, thought that the changing sky was somewhat like the walls at Radio City Music Hall just after the show had ended. They both grew lighter very gradually, going from a purple to a dark blue to a light blue with pink around the edges. He thought that he was lucky even to see dawn over the Pacific, for the fact was that it had cost Spitzer a great deal to get to wear a uniform. A very high temperature during a childhood illness had caused his eyes to cross slightly. He had been flatly turned down for service, and had had to have two serious eye operations before the Army Air Force would accept him. Since then, he had wondered more than once exactly why he had gone to all that trouble. Maybe this mission was the answer.

Jimmy Van Pelt was checking and rechecking his navigation. He guessed that he had done more celestial fixes than ever before. As they had passed Iwo Jima, he had gotten a Loran (long range) navigation check and another radio confirmation. He couldn't take any chances. With the critical fuel situation, he knew that he had to get them to the rendezvous point, then to the target, without any hitches. A navigational error—no matter how small—could be disastrous.

Flight Engineer John Kuharek was still watching the fuel gauges, but with even greater anxiety than before. When they began to climb in about half an hour, the problem would intensify. At 31,000 feet and with the weight of the bomb, fuel consumption would be very rapid—over 1,000 gallons an hour. Every now and then, Kuharek would jot down some figures, trying to compute from rate of speed, rpm, fuel consumption and average altitude whether they would have enough gas to get home again. Each time the figures gave him the same answer. They would make it—*if* there were no delays along the way.

Research Technician Goro Tao was depressed. He had come early that Thursday to his laboratory in the Nagasaki prefecture building for purely selfish reasons. This British-designed, two-story-high concrete structure, particularly his laboratory in the basement, was one of the coolest spots in town. The heat and humidity over the past three weeks had been almost unbearable even for the southern Kyushuans who were used to it. Every day the temperature had climbed high into the 90's, and the evenings had provided little relief, seldom dropping lower than 85 or 86. Sleep had been difficult for him, so it was with a genuine feeling of relief that Mr. Tao entered the prefecture building that morning and sat down in his chair in the basement. It was wonderfully cool.

A little later, pausing for a cup of tea, he stood by the first-floor window, looking out at the square, and the depression that he had been experiencing in recent days came upon him once again. It was senseless to continue a war that was already lost, he thought, then glanced around guiltily, as if afraid that someone might be reading his thoughts. But the corridor was empty. Down the street, near Nagasaki Station, he could see a long line of small schoolgirls being moved to the country. In the square, soldiers were drilling with bamboo poles instead of guns. He sighed. How could they possibly fight the Americans with bamboo poles? It was silly, just as silly as trying to camouflage the important buildings in the city. Even the prefecture building had been partly covered with black paint, slapped on carelessly as though by a frustrated, impatient artist. How ridiculous! You can't really disguise a shipbuilding yard, or a huge arms manufacturing plant. The Americans were not quite as stupid as some people tried to picture them.

Sometime after eight, the air-raid alarm sounded. Earlier than usual, he thought. Well, at least we won't have to spend our lunch hour in the dugout. Mr. Tao, along with his colleagues, went out the back door of the building through the laboratory to the dugout built into the hillside under a cliff. When the all-clear sounded, he and the others slowly returned to their offices. His colleague, Mr. Yoshikawa, had come in late that morning and had missed the drill. Now he stopped Mr. Tao in the corridor to tell him a long, unfunny story. Tao laughed as convincingly as he could so as not to hurt the older man's feelings, then made his way down to his laboratory in the basement. It was cool and he sighed as he sat down. He would have given a day's pay for a cigarette right then.

0700 HOURS

COMMANDER ASHWORTH ON BOARD *Bock's Car* HAD JUST LIT A cigarette. He drew the smoke in deeply but his eyes never left the black box in front of him. Beside him sat Lieutenant Barnes, also staring at the red light on the side of the box as it blinked in slow, measured rhythm. That steady light said, in effect, that the electrical circuits and the three sets of fuses within the bomb were functioning correctly. But if the red light began to act like a fibrillating heart—wild and out of control—it meant that one of many possible things had gone wrong. A short-circuited condenser or a loose wire could be repaired. Even if one of the barometric pressure fuses had somehow been activated, there was no danger unless the plane should suddenly drop to 1,500 feet. If an electronic fuse were activated, the bomb would have been detonated immediately. It was the thought of any possible malfunction in the third set of fuses, the time fuses, that caused Ashworth to stare so intently at the red light. It had been calculated that it took precisely fifty-two seconds for this particular bomb to drop to 1,500 feet. If a time fuse were to cause trouble, Ashworth and Barnes would have fifty-two seconds to fix it, or else . . .

Behind the black box was the bomb itself, and Ashworth found himself regarding it with fascination. Four and a half feet wide, ten and a half feet long, it looked like a giant, tapered watermelon—a 10,000-pound watermelon. Twelve hours earlier, Ashworth and the scientists on Tinian had put the final touches on the arming mechanisms. Now it was not only ugly—but dangerous. But would it work?

The waiting to find out was actually the hardest part for him, the "weaponeer." Although he had a good idea of the bomb's incredible power, he still could not be absolutely certain it would perform in battle. No one could. This deadly little toy had cost billions of dollars, had involved hundreds of thousands of men, the most creative and resourceful minds in the scientific community, and an amazingly cohesive partnership between industrial production and the technicians and scientists who had designed it. And *still* no one could guarantee the results. Fat Man's predecessor had worked less than a month ago on a barren, scorching New Mexico desert called *Jornada del Muerto,* the Journey of Death.

Ashworth himself had been there, one of a select group of military men, and had seen the awesome force unleashed for the first time. Captain "Deke" Parsons, who had been in charge of the bomb on the Hiroshima mission, had been there too. Both men had earlier witnessed the transformation of the New Mexico desert into a scientific beehive and both knew some of the problems the Manhattan Project had had to solve in translating nuclear theory into atomic fact. Ashworth and Parsons had come to know that incredible band of creative scientists who had dreamed and persevered, from Enrico Fermi—the ultimate genius among geniuses who had initiated the first nuclear chain reaction—to Richard Feynman who, at a rebellious and precocious 27, loved to thwart the censors in that super-secret community by shredding his letters into tiny pieces before sending them out. "They are for my wife," he would explain to infuriated security men who had no way of deciphering the bits of paper. "She is very sick, in the hospital, and she assembles these letters like jigsaw puzzles. It is therapy for her. You understand?"

It had been a time of discovery for Ashworth. A graduate of the U. S. Naval Academy (Class of '33), he had had postgraduate training in aviation ordnance, had commanded a torpedo squadron and served on the staff of Amphibious Forces, Pacific. Tapped in 1944 for the Manhattan Project, he soon found himself involved in the greatest undertaking he had ever seen. The 35-year-old lieutenant commander from Beverly, Massachusetts, had never imagined that he would ever be in the company of such extraordinary people. "Deke" Parsons, also a career Navy man, apparently felt the same way, for he once told Ashworth this story: One evening at Los Alamos, the Parsonses entertained a group of friends, mostly neighbors and civilian colleagues working on the project. The evening went well, and at one point Nan Parsons turned to her husband and smiled. "You know, Deke," she said in wonder, "it just occurred to me. Every single man in this room—except you—is a Nobel Prize winner."

Ashworth was also probably the only man aboard *Bock's Car* who understood completely how Fat Man worked. It sounded like a complicated process, but like so many problems, once figured out, the principle was simple. The plutonium core of Fat Man was divided into two hemispheres, like a melon sliced in half. These half-globes were placed in the center of a ring of explosive charges ingeniously arranged to press in on the core simultaneously when triggered by an electric current. The theory was that the explosion would drive the two hemispheres together and achieve "critical mass," in other words set off a fantastically rapid chain reaction, splitting billions of plutonium nuclei and releasing their combined energy—all within a millionth of a second. But *would it work* this time? They would know in a few hours.

Somewhere in the sky behind Ashworth, the instrument plane, *The Great Artiste,* was also racing toward the rendezvous point. Aboard her, reporter Bill Laurence wrote in his notebook: "I am riding above the giant mountains of white cumulous clouds, letting myself be suspended in infinite space. One hears the whir of the motors, but it soon becomes insignificant against the immensity all around and before long one is swallowed by it. There comes a point where space also swallows time and one lives through eternal moments filled with an oppressive loneliness, as though all life had suddenly vanished from the earth, and you are the only one left, a lone survivor traveling endlessly through interplanetary space."

In the third plane, the one carrying the photo equipment, Major Jim Hopkins was trying to absorb the instructions he had received a little while earlier. Just before takeoff, Dr. Robert Serber, the expert in high-speed photography, had turned up without his parachute. Hopkins had ordered him to get it, but the plane was already airborne when he returned with his chute. Crestfallen, Serber had reported to General Farrell, who decided to break radio silence. For some twenty minutes after Farrell got through to Hopkins, Serber had given radio instructions to him on the proper use of the special photo equipment. Hopkins hoped he had it all straight in his mind.

Back on Sweeney's plane, in one instant, things went terribly wrong. Ashworth was dozing when Barnes grabbed his arm, jolting him awake. "Commander, look!" The voice was sharp.

Ashworth's eyes leaped to the black box. The red light had begun to flash wildly and irregularly. My God! he thought. It's happened! For a second he sat frozen, then whirled to Barnes. "Let's have a look! Quick!"

But Barnes, trained for just such an emergency, had already begun to remove the cover of the box. He had not wasted one second. Although such a thing had never actually happened, Barnes had gone through the possibility of just such an event many times in his mind. As a starting procedure, he had been provided with four key points to check, and he quickly ran them through. The check revealed nothing wrong, yet the red light continued to flash warningly. There were several options open to him now. One would be to trace each electrical circuit in the black box; but even if he could put his finger on the critical spot within each circuit that would tell him if the trouble lay within that area, he would still have hundreds of circuits to investigate, and such a procedure could take hours. He could check the entire circuit clockwise, then counterclockwise to confirm—again, a matter of hours.

Ashworth was glancing anxiously at his watch. How much time had gone by already? Why hadn't he marked the instant of trouble right away? No matter. It was too late now. "How about the time fuses?" he asked anxiously.

Barnes was frowning in concentration, his eyes narrowed in intense study of the complex mechanism. "They're OK, I think," he said absently. He made up his mind what to do. Intuitively, like an expert diagnostician, he had begun to put himself mentally through the wire circuit, testing, evaluating each critical junction as he reached it in his mind. His fingers, translating the mind's directions, darted nimbly through the interior maze of wires and switches and coils. They sped along wires, trying to feel slices, breaks, severed connections, anything that would jar his sense of touch. The black box might be the monitor of the bomb, but he, a mere human, was the monitor of the box.

Barnes' grandfather had been a doctor, a general practitioner, and many times the doctor had taken his young grandson along on his country rounds. Occasionally, he had taken the boy into his confidence and explained a patient's symptoms. Now Phil remembered one case in particular. The patient, a boy about his own age, had had a galloping bellyache, and the old doctor, poking gently on the boy's abdomen, had said to his grandson: "Once you find out that the stomach muscles aren't hard, chances are that it's not serious."

"But then why does it hurt, Grandpa?" he had asked.

"Could be a lotta things. Let's see, the parents say the

food was all right, so that's out. Now it could be gas. Gas can give you some bellyache, I'll tell you. But that don't last long. In this case, I'd bet that it's a big chunk of chuck roast—they had that for dinner, you know—that didn't get chewed all up. The stomach juices couldn't make much of a dent in it, and I'll bet that big hunk of meat went right into the intestines and got stuck. Then Mama Nature took over the only way the body knows how—she sent out a signal telling us that something was wrong. And the way she does that, my boy, is simple: she gives us a helluva pain!"

That was exactly what the black box was doing now, he thought; it was informing him that it had a "helluva pain" and that he better find out what was causing it. Then, as his eyes followed the blueprint of the electrical circuitry and his fingers, tracing the physical wiring, confirmed what he read, he suddenly found it! Two small rotary switches should have been in positions two and three, respectively. When his fingers told him that their positions were actually reversed, he looked inside and saw that it was indeed true. Apparently, a mistake had been made in the arming process, but the current, although taking an alternate route through another circuit, had negotiated the journey without any trouble. Unfortunately, the monitor had not been programmed to accept this substitute path, and could only assume that something had gone wrong. He had no idea why it hadn't acted before this.

Barnes flipped the two tiny switches into their proper positions, and, just like that, the red light stopped its warning irregular signal and began to blink steadily once more. He looked across at Ashworth. "We got it," he said softly.

"What was it?" Ashworth was actually conscious of his heartbeat slowing.

"Couple of switches improperly set."

"A couple of switches! My God!"

Both men seemed content for the moment merely to sit

and watch the red light flash on and off with monotonous regularity. It had never looked so good.

"One thing we know it *wasn't*," Barnes added.

"What's that?"

"We know it wasn't the time fuses." He smiled at Ashworth, who smiled back weakly. They had been through a great deal together in a very short time.

Ashworth glanced at his watch. About ten minutes, he estimated. They were all damn lucky to have had a man like Lieutenant Philip Barnes aboard.

Up front, Chuck Sweeney was about to begin his climb to rendezvous altitude—31,000 feet. Somehow he must have sensed something amiss, for he called Ashworth on the intercom. "Pilot to weaponeer: Everything all right, Dick?"

Ashworth wiped the sweat from his forehead. He had been about to report to Sweeney. "Nothing to worry about—now," he replied. "I'll come up and fill you in." He moved forward and seconds later was telling Sweeney exactly what had just happened.

Sweeney's hands gripped the control column tightly as Ashworth talked. When he finished, Sweeney took a deep breath and let it out very slowly. "Oh, Lord," he whispered.

Glancing back, Sweeney could see the top of the bomb, yellow with black tail fins and obscene and explicit messages written on it, and he began to speculate on the immense power that lay within that shell. The decision of whether or not to drop the bomb was one with which he had never concerned himself. That was a moral, a political, a grand-strategy decision, and he was a simple soldier trying to do his job as well as he could. He was like most bomber pilots who have formed a defensive armor about their particular role in war. Their function is to drop bombs on targets, not on people. Were they to think otherwise, to be ordered to drop a bomb on, say, 2,567 men, women and children, they would probably go mad. A target was a different matter; a target didn't live or breathe or hurt. Still, Sweeney had seen the effects of this kind of bomb at Hiroshima, and he knew, deep within himself, that there had been people down there, enemies though they were. Now, the decision had been made to drop another one. At that moment, he was glad he had not had to make it.

CHAPTER 3

Command Decision

0600 HOURS
(8:00 P.M., AUGUST 8, EASTERN WAR TIME, WASHINGTON, D.C.)

THE MAN RESPONSIBLE FOR MAKING THAT DECISION WAS AT the moment sitting behind a large desk on which, in later years, a placard would bluntly inform visitors that "The Buck Stops Here." On that evening, August 8, 1945, it would have been an especially appropriate sentiment. For in the final decision of whether or not to drop the second atomic bomb on the people of Japan, President Harry S. Truman had no one to pass the buck to.

Roosevelt's concern over that painful decision had "worried him terribly." Harry Truman, on the other hand, seemed more pragmatic about the situation, although he too was fully aware of the enormous moral burden that accompanied any decision he might make. Later he would put it: "Worry is often the interest on a debt that never comes due. I can't afford to worry. I am a simple man." He was from Missouri, and the hard facts kept his eyes focused straight ahead: The war had to be won, won as quickly and with as little loss of American life as possible. How could that best be accomplished? That was the question he would address himself to in the first months of his Presidency.

Actually, when he took over the world's most demanding job, the Man from Missouri had had only four months to acquaint himself with the duties and responsibilities of the Vice-Presidency. Then, with shattering suddenness, had come the elevation to the Presidency itself. It was only after Harry Truman had officially become the thirty-third President of the United States, that he had become fully aware of just how little he knew about his predecessor's activities and plans. Roosevelt had been virtually a one-man show; although he had listened to his Cabinet members, he had kept his own counsel to a large extent, and in that regard he had been his own Secretary of the Treasury, his own Secretary of State, his own Secretary of War.

For the 61-year-old Truman, former farmer, bank clerk, postmaster, haberdasher, and a politician for twenty years, the challenge of the Presidency was formidable indeed, and one which he had neither sought nor wanted. When he had received from Mrs. Roosevelt the shocking news that the President was dead, he had immediately thought that few men in history equaled the one into whose shoes he was stepping, and he had prayed to God that he could measure up to the job.

During those early days as President, Harry Truman's major task had been to familiarize himself with the state of the nation's affairs, and he soon discovered that regarding one project in particular he was completely in the dark. He had first heard of the existence of the atomic bomb project exactly *one hour* after his inauguration as President of the United States. After a brief Cabinet meeting, Secretary of War Stimson, who probably knew more about the entire undertaking than any other government official, took the new President aside, saying that he must talk to him about a most urgent matter. He then asked Truman whether he had ever heard anything about a top-secret undertaking called the Manhattan Project. The President shook his head, saying that Roosevelt had never mentioned those particular words to him. The Manhattan Project, Stimson explained briefly, was a massive, billion-dollar attempt to develop "a new explosive of unbelievable destructive power."

Although the news came as a complete surprise to Truman, he had almost stumbled on the great secret two years earlier when he had been only an inquisitive Senator from Missouri. At that time, members of the special committee to investigate the national defense program, of which he had been chairman, had been refused admittance to a mysterious government project at Oak Ridge, Tennessee. Truman had kicked up quite a fuss about not being allowed to inspect the plant until that same Stimson had called him up. "Senator, I can't tell you what it is, but it's the greatest project in the history of the world," Stimson had confided. "It is most top-secret. You understand?" Truman had understood. "You don't have to say another word to me," he had promised and had dropped his inspection demands.

Shortly after Truman's first brief Cabinet meeting and Stimson's cryptic remarks to him, Dr. Vannevar Bush, head of the Office of Scientific Research and Development, had called upon the new President and explained what he and his fellow scientists were trying to do. The next day, James Byrnes, who would soon be Truman's Secretary of State, added his own comments. Byrnes told him in effect that this explosive that the United States was at the moment perfecting was great enough to destroy the world. This new atomic bomb, he said, "might well put us in a position to dictate our own terms at the end of the war."

A few days later, Truman received even more precise and

detailed information about the progress of the Manhattan Project. Stimson presented him with a memo which stated unequivocally that "within four months we shall in all probability have completed the most terrible weapon ever known in human history, one bomb of which could destroy a whole city. The world," he concluded gravely, "will eventually be at the mercy of such a weapon." General Leslie R. Groves, military director of the project, then gave the President a complete report on the history of the Manhattan Project, which, he said, had already required the services of 100,000 men and had cost two and a half billion dollars over a two-and-a-half-year period—a cost, he added, which amounted to almost *three million dollars a day*. To justify this expense, he concluded, a bomb would soon be ready which had an anticipated explosive force of between 10,000 and 20,000 tons of TNT. To his visitors, Truman seemed impressed, but hardly astounded, which is understandable. At that time it was almost impossible for laymen to conceive of that kind of explosive power. It was new to mankind, a totally unknown force. Truman himself admitted that by way of comparison, he immediately thought of something with which he was familiar. He had been an artillery captain in World War I, and he said that the picture that sprang into his mind was the explosions caused by the Big Bertha artillery shells used during that war.

Now that the bomb had progressed from a possibility to a probability, the President wondered whether target cities had been chosen—assuming, of course, that the bomb would be used. The targets had already been chosen, he was assured. General Groves, under orders from General Marshall, had drawn up a list of criteria for the selection of suitable Japanese cities. Each target, he had concluded, must be military in nature, either a troop concentration, a port, or a supply center of strategic materials; it must be undamaged by previous bombing attacks, so that the full destructive effects of the bomb could readily be seen and undisputably evaluated; it must be of such an importance that its destruction would "most adversely affect the will of the Japanese people to continue the war."

Eventually, four targets had been selected: Kokura, which had one of the largest munition plants in Japan, Hiroshima, a main port of embarkation, Niigata, an important port in the Japan Sea, and Kyoto, described by Groves as "an urban industrial area with a population of about a million inhabitants." All were considered suitable and were passed along to Stimson for approval.

That approval would probably have been immediately forthcoming had it not been for a seemingly trivial coincidence. Early that spring, Stimson had been paid a visit by an acquaintance who happened to be a student of Oriental history. During the course of the evening the visitor had filled Stimson's ear with descriptions of the lovely old capital city of Kyoto and its colorful and glorious history as the cultural center of Japan. So it was that when Stimson was presented with the selected targets, his first comment was, "No. I don't like it. I don't like the use of Kyoto." He struck it from the list and another city was added, a port city in which the Mitsubishi shipbuilding and arms factories were located. In such a way was Nagasaki doomed.

Now, on that August evening, as Harry Truman sat behind his big desk staring down at a piece of paper he held, he found himself thinking of the events that had transpired over the past four months. It had been a crisis-ridden time of decision. During that period he had had to deal with some of the most crucial problems ever faced by a U. S. President in so short a time. For one thing, there was the inherited agreement made by Roosevelt and Churchill at Yalta that Japan must surrender unconditionally. Tied in with that was the question of whether to allow the Emperor to remain in power after the war. Acting Secretary of State Joseph Grew had told the President that he believed that "if the Japanese are permitted to determine their own future political structure, they will be afforded a method of saving face without which surrender will be highly unlikely." Dean Acheson had disagreed violently. He considered the institution of the throne "an anachronistic, feudal institution perfectly adapted to the use of anachronistic, feudal-minded groups within the country." Furthermore, with the intense prejudice of Americans against the Emperor that then existed, he was convinced that Congress would never go along with any plan to retain Hirohito as Emperor.

Truman also faced the problem of evaluating the importance of securing Russia's entry into the Pacific war. Stalin had promised that three months after Germany surrendered, the Soviet Union would declare war on Japan. But many State Department people had been having second thoughts about such an action. Russia's grasping and intransigent attitude in Eastern Europe—particularly with regard to Poland and Bulgaria—had made some people uneasy about her future participation in the war against Japan. Averell Harriman had warned flatly that unless a stiffer attitude was adopted, all of Europe might be communist by winter. Consequently, many people now believed that the Soviet Union must not be given a strong bargaining position in Asia which her early involvement in the Pacific war might lead her to expect and demand.

Unfortunately, the President discovered that this tenor of thinking ran smack into the plans of the military and the Joint Chiefs. Those military who knew of the existence of the bomb were frankly skeptical of the scientists' predictions. Admiral William D. Leahy, the chief of staff to the President, declared in no uncertain words that the thing would never work. "This is the biggest fool thing we have ever done," he had told Truman. "The bomb will never go off, and I speak as an expert in explosives." As a result, the military leaders were proceeding on the assumption that the only prudent course of action to pursue was the continuation and enlargement of the war effort, culminating in an invasion of the Japanese mainland itself. In fact, an actual invasion of the island of Kyushu—code-named Olympic—had already been scheduled for November 1, 1945, to be followed by a second invasion of the Kanto Plains near Tokyo—code-named Coronet. All admitted, however, that such a landing was bound to be horribly costly in American lives, and that the war could easily go on for another year and a half. The ferocious defense of Okinawa by 100,000 fanatics suggested that the Japanese were determined to fight to the very end. There were still over six million Japanese troops to defend the main islands, and many military men estimated that there would be a million or more Allied casualties in an invasion of the mainland. Stimson had warned the President that there might be a million American casualties alone.

Therefore the military wanted a firm commitment from Stalin as to when the Soviets planned to enter the war against Japan and invade Manchuria from the north. Intelligence experts had located at least ten Japanese divisions in that area, and reasoned that if they could be tied up in Manchuria, it would make the invasion from the south that much easier. Douglas MacArthur had put it this way: "The hazard and loss will be greatly lessened if a Soviet attack is launched from Siberia sufficiently ahead of our target date to commit the enemy to major combat."

With different and often conflicting advice pressing in from all sides, Truman realized that he would have to meet with Stalin to get this question settled. The problem was one of timing. The military urged swift action and so did Winston Churchill, who wanted an early meeting so that the British could establish a timetable for regaining control of their colonial possessions in Southeast Asia. It was Stimson who urged caution, who advised the President to wait at least until the new bomb had been tested at Alamogordo. For more than anyone else, it was Stimson who now regarded the atomic bomb as America's ace in the hole, a sudden, decisive tool for putting an end to the bloodshed and a potential political weapon of unguessed power. And it was Stimson to whom Truman finally listened—and acquiesced. The bomb test would take place on July 16. The Potsdam Conference would begin that same day, and it was hoped that the most potent ammunition at the President's disposal—the new atomic bomb—would indeed be available.

That one question—whether or not to use the bomb and, if so, exactly how to use it—was to remain Truman's overriding concern during June and July. To help him with the delicate and complex considerations—administrative, political, military and moral—connected with the fruits of the Manhattan Project, Stimson had earlier suggested the formation of an interim committee, entirely made up of some of the civilians (even General Groves was not included) most familiar with it, and a scientific advisory panel consisting of J. Robert Oppenheimer, the director of the Los Alamos Laboratory, Dr. Arthur H. Compton in the Chicago end of the project, Dr. Ernest O. Lawrence, the director of the Berkeley Radiation Laboratory, and Enrico Fermi, the guiding light behind the Chicago experiments.

These two groups, among others, had to offer advice to the Man from Missouri about such questions as: Should the bomb actually be used against the population of Japan in the hope that the war could be terminated swiftly and an invasion avoided? How much should the Russians be told about the new weapon? Should the Japanese receive a prior warning about the nature of what they might expect from such a bomb, perhaps through a demonstration? Were two bombs necessary to produce the desired effect on the war party in Japan? In answer to the last query, General Groves thought two bombs were a minimum. One was needed to demonstrate the terrible power of the weapon. The second would convince the Japanese militarists that the United States had more than a single bomb at its disposal.

Gradually, all the questions were dealt with, though not to everyone's satisfaction by any means. The Interim Committee and the Scientific Advisory Panel eventually had to agree with Secretary Stimson that the use of the bomb on Japan offered the best hope for ending the war quickly and with the fewest American casualties. As for the question of giving the Japanese advance warning, the prevailing opinion was against doing so. For one thing, the bomb might be a dud. Also, Secretary Byrnes feared that if a certain locality were to be named as the target site, the Japanese might bring American prisoners-of-war to that area. But the most important reason for not giving detailed advance warning was the Stimson-oriented opinion that any such announcement of the impending use of the new weapon would invalidate one of the main purposes of the bomb, namely, to "shock" the Japanese into surrender by use of the terrible bomb. Thinking back on that one point, Truman was glad that the decision had been at least partly modified. Leaflets were going to be dropped on the selected cities a few days prior to bombing which would warn the people what was to come and advise them to leave their cities.

The question of a demonstration of the bomb had actually become one of the most controversial aspects of the entire A-bomb program. The two advisory groups, once they had reluctantly recommended the bomb's use, were immediately confronted with the objections of a number of scientists who seriously doubted the international morality of a surprise atomic-bomb attack on Japan. These scientists, including James Franck, Leo Szilard, Eugene Rabinowitch and Glenn T. Seaborg, put their objections into words in a document called "The Franck Report" which stated that "the use of nuclear bombs for an early unannounced attack against Japan is unadvisable." These scientists had then suggested "a demonstration of the new weapon to be made before the eyes of the representatives of all the United Nations on the desert or on a barren island." Other Manhattan Project scientists had already suggested that a demonstration in an isolated part of Japan, or over Tokyo Bay, or very high in the atmosphere, might be enough to convince the Japanese militarists of the bomb's destructive powers.

The arguments against these proposals had been equally convincing. Again, there was the possibility that the bomb might be a dud, in which case the demonstration would backfire and very possibly give a psychological boost to enemy morale. In the end, however, it was J. Robert Oppenheimer who tilted the scales in favor of using the bomb directly. Later, he would say sadly, "We had known the sin of pride, of thinking we knew what was good for man. That is not the business of scientists." But at that unforgettable moment in history a different kind of pride had been involved, the pride of incredible accomplishment. And, to be sure, the country was still at war, and perhaps the bomb would end it all quickly. Finally, it was Oppenheimer who posed the question: "Will the Japanese Government, divided as it is between the peace party and the war party, be decisively influenced by an enormous nuclear firecracker detonated at great height, or doing little damage?" To the Interim Committee, to the Scientific Advisory Panel, to Secretary Byrnes, to Secretary Stimson—and to President Harry Truman—the answer seemed obvious. *No.*

Those were the moments that Truman now remembered, and there were others, brief scenes but etched in his mind. There was the day, just before the start of the Potsdam Conference, when he had been taken on a tour of Berlin. His motorcade traveled from Babelsberg along the Autobahn to the center of Berlin, down Wilhelmstrasse to the gutted remains of the *Reichskanzlei,* Hitler's tomb. Truman had passed by the ruins of the Reichstag, the Sports Palace, and dozens of other once-famous sites which now were only piles of stone and rubble. He had been depressed by the ruined buildings, and by the old men and women and children walking aimlessly along the pockmarked streets carrying what was left of their belongings. He thought that he had never seen such utter destruction. "That's what happens," he had murmured, "when man overreaches himself." At that time he had not been informed of the successful A-bomb test at Alamogordo. And so he had no way of realizing the comparison that lay before him, that even after three and a half years of constant bombardment, the city of Berlin had sustained less damage than would soon result from the atomic bombs about to be dropped on Japan, or that the one bomb dropped on Nagasaki would kill more people than German air attacks on London killed during the entire war.

There was that evening at Potsdam when Stimson had informed him of the results of the A-bomb test at Alamogordo. A disguised message had arrived, Stimson said, which read: "Doctor has just returned most enthusiastic and confident that the little boy is as husky as his big brother. The light in his eyes was discernible from here to Highhold and I could have heard his screams from here to my farm."

Translated, this meant in effect that Groves had returned from the test site confident that the plutonium bomb was just as potent as the untested uranium bomb already on its way to Tinian. The light of the test explosion, he reported, could be seen 250 miles away and heard for a distance of 50 miles. This indicated that the test had been far more successful than anyone could have hoped. Truman was delighted with the realization that this immense undertaking had been completed with such dramatic success. It was at that moment that he actually realized what he now had at his disposal. The atomic bomb was not an abstract theory that might or might not work. The atomic bomb was a reality. The Atomic Age had started.

There was also the moment when he had first told Stalin about the new weapon that the United States had just perfected. For months there had been a running controversy both within the government and among the scientists over just how much to tell the Soviets about the new bomb. Both the Interim Committee and the Scientific Advisory Panel had urged that the Soviet Union and our other allies be informed about the whole project *before* the bomb was dropped. But Stimson, Byrnes and Churchill all were leery of telling Stalin anything more than the barest minimum and Truman had agreed to do just that. He had informed Churchill of his decision: "I think I had best just tell him after one of our meetings that we have an entirely novel form of bomb, something quite out of the ordinary, which we think will have a decisive effect on the Japanese will to continue the war." If the Soviet leader then pressed for further details, he would be informed that it was premature to discuss such matters at that time. Churchill had concurred.

After the July 24 formal meeting between the Big Three had ended, the opportunity presented itself. Truman strolled over to Stalin and his interpreter and remarked as casually as he could: "By the way, Premier Stalin, I thought you might be interested in knowing that the United States has developed a new weapon of unusual destructive force." To Truman's astonishment, Stalin seemed totally unimpressed, remarking politely that he hoped that the United States would "make good use of it against the Japanese." Secretary Byrnes, who had observed the encounter with intense interest, confirmed Truman's impression: "I watched Mr. Stalin's face as the President made this statement and I was of the opinion that Stalin did not grasp its importance."

Again, Truman had no way of knowing it then, but possibly Stalin knew almost as much about the atomic bomb as Truman did. Klaus Fuchs and David Greenglass, working in ultrasensitive positions at Los Alamos for the last two years, had compiled the most detailed plans of the bomb's inner workings and passed them along to Harry Gold and the Rosenbergs for transmission to the Soviet Union. It is hardly surprising that Joseph Stalin, that inscrutable old poker player, did not seem as impressed as he should have been if, after all, he knew what Truman's "hole card" was.

Now that the bomb was a reality, Truman had to decide how best to make use of this sensational new weapon. The Big Three agreed to warn Japan of what lay ahead for her should she not surrender. On July 25, the Potsdam Declaration was issued, which called upon the government of Japan "to proclaim now the unconditional surrender of all Japanese armed forces. The alternative for Japan," it warned ominously, "is prompt and utter destruction."

In the days after that uncompromising statement there was only silence from Tokyo. Then, on July 28, Radio Tokyo announced that the Japanese Government was determined to continue to fight. It labeled the Potsdam Declaration "unworthy of consideration" and "absurd." Now Truman had to act. Accordingly, on his recommendation, a memo was sent to General Carl Spaatz, commanding general of the U. S. Strategic Air Forces, which directed the 509th Composite Group, 20th Air Force, to "deliver its first special bomb as soon as weather will permit after 3 August 1945 on one of the targets: Hiroshima, Kokura, Niigata or Nagasaki." The memo also stated that "additional bombs will be delivered on the above targets as soon as made ready by the project staff." Groves had told Truman that a third bomb would be available by August 19, and a fourth ten days later, if they were necessary. General Spaatz had been given latitude as to which targets should finally be chosen and when the bombs would be delivered, pending weather conditions.

The die had been cast. Truman's thoughts at the time reflect his conviction that he had done the only thing possible. "With this order the wheels were set in motion for the first use of an atomic weapon against a military target. I had made the decision. There was no alternative. I also instructed Stimson that the order to Spaatz should stand unless I notified him that the Japanese reply to our ultimatum was accepted."

Now, sitting behind his White House desk, Harry Truman realized that yet another decision had to be made. In his hand was a copy of the message sent by "Deke" Parsons, who had armed the bomb which had been dropped on Hiroshima two days earlier. "Results of bomb clear-cut and successful," the message read in matter-of-fact fashion. "Visible effects greater than in any test."

Truman remembered how he had felt when he had first heard the news about the Hiroshima bomb-drop. He had turned to a group of sailors on board the *Augusta,* the ship that was carrying him back to the States from Potsdam, and explained: "This is the greatest thing in history." At that moment he had been absolutely convinced that the Pacific war could now be brought to a speedy end.

Shortly after that first bomb, the President had issued the following statement: "It was to spare the Japanese people from utter destruction that the ultimatum of July 26 was issued at Potsdam. Their leaders promptly rejected that ultimatum. If they do not now accept our terms, they may expect a rain of ruin from the air the likes of which has never been seen on this earth."

But no surrender offer had come, and now he had to make the choice once more. Should the atomic bombing be continued? The latest reports from Hiroshima had confirmed the fact that the devastation of that city had been intense and widespread. Unless he acted immediately, the order to General Spaatz to proceed as directed would stand. Why in the name of God hadn't the Japanese given some concrete indication that they were considering surrender? Couldn't they realize that he meant what he said, that prompt and utter destruction would surely follow unless they accepted the ultimatum? And now Russia had entered the war, complicating the picture and requiring a speeding up of the whole timetable.

President Harry S. Truman crumpled the piece of paper, the report from Parsons, and threw it in the wastebasket. He really had no choice. The order to General Spaatz would stand. The second bomb would have to be dropped.

CHAPTER 4

The Gentle Doctor

0630 HOURS

EVEN AS MAJOR SWEENEY WAS WINGING OVER THE BLUE PACIFIC, and Harry Truman was crumpling a piece of paper, Dr. Sakurai in Nagasaki was dreaming of water. The night before, he had taken a walk and had run into Deputy Mayor Morita who was strangely upset. He had told the doctor that on his way home, he had had to leave the streetcar because the Ibinokuchi River had overflowed its banks. Such a thing had never happened before, as far as he knew, and for some reason he considered it an ill omen, a portent of coming disaster. "Something terrible will happen tomorrow," he had intoned. Now, Dr. Sakurai was dreaming of water creeping slowly up until it covered his chin, his mouth, his eyes. . . . He woke up, bathed in sweat. Then he smiled sheepishly at the silliness of the dream and went back to sleep.

An hour later, he arose, washed and ate the simple breakfast his mother prepared. It was time for him to go to the hospital. There was much to do. He had forgotten all about his dream.

To many people of Nagasaki, he was known as the Gentle Doctor. Perhaps it was because he was frail and small—frail even in a nation of small people, his hands delicate and long-fingered. Or maybe it was because he himself had been a sickly child, and during his young life had become well acquainted with illness and discomfort. Or perhaps it was because he was the only boy in a family of girls and some of the gentler qualities of that sex had rubbed off on him. In any case, for those people who thought of him as the Gentle Doctor, he seemed to possess an extra ingredient of gentleness, a little measure more of that special tender quality that can make other people feel at ease, less in pain, understood.

His name was Hachiroemon Sakurai: he was 26 years old, and one of the two doctors at the Catholic Nagasaki First Branch Hospital overlooking the Urakami Valley. Of the forty-odd beds in the hospital, some 60 percent were occupied by TB patients. The other beds were filled with such patients as you would find in any hospital—postnatal cases, infectious disease patients, one post-surgical case, and four cases of acute malnutrition. The latter especially worried Dr. Sakurai. Four cases were more than they had ever had before, and he was becoming increasingly alarmed at the prevalence of acute malnutrition. Still, there was not very much he could do about it. For at that moment in Japan's history, there was just not enough food to go around.

On that Thursday morning, as he walked from his parents' house the half mile to the hospital, Dr. Sakurai observed that there were only a few scattered clouds in the sky, and that the wide expanse of blue, coupled with the shrill chirruping of the cicadas, gave ample warning of another sweltering day ahead. As he entered the front door, Brother Mizuiwa, a Franciscan monk who was almost as broad as he was tall, approached to tell him that four new X-ray machines had been delivered to the hospital last night for safekeeping in the basement. The directors of two other hospitals in the downtown section felt that the Nagasaki First Branch Hospital was likely to be the most protected medical building in the area in the event of any large-scale bombing.

In his office, Nurse Emiko Ozaki, trim and smiling, greeted him. "Good morning. We already have a full house and it's only just after eight o'clock."

"They're waiting already, eh? Well, we better get started with our eager patients."

She nodded and disappeared quickly into the outer office. Nurse Ozaki had been in this hospital for only two months, yet Dr. Sakurai had already become quite dependent on her. That was surprising, considering what her attitude had been when she first came to the hospital. For the first week there, she had seemed to resent the smallness of the place, having come from a much larger and better-equipped establishment. She had been uncooperative, almost surly, until Dr. Sakurai had taken her aside and explained as gently as he could: "Nurse Ozaki, I quite understand that this poor hospital is far inferior to the grand institution you have been used to. But please believe me, the people here are just as sick. They need you just as much as the patients needed you there. Shall we devote ourselves to *their* welfare and try to forget our unimportant little differences?"

That brief statement seemed to work wonders with her, and she had changed almost overnight. Her scowl had been replaced by an astonishingly white smile, and her warm-hearted nature had asserted itself at once. Now, even more than his woman colleague, Dr. Yuriko Miyazaki, she had become his indispensable right arm, anticipating his requests and handling the routine, obvious cases without even disturbing him.

By nine o'clock that morning, the number of people in the waiting room had swelled to more than thirty. He called in Nurse Ozaki and asked: "How many of those waiting outside require pneumothorax treatment?" The withdrawal by needle of any fluid that had accumulated in the lungs was not a complicated process, but it was a time-consuming one.

"At least ten, Doctor."

"Very well. Would you ask Dr. Miyazaki if she could handle those cases?"

Nurse Ozaki smiled her lovely white smile. "I already took that liberty. She said she would be happy to take them."

There was a knock on the door, and the face of Engineer Kunio Tayama peered around the edge of it. "Am I interrupting anything important?"

"Not at all," the doctor said cheerfully. "Come on in." He was always glad to see the crew-cut, broad-faced scientist.

"Thank you," said the other, pushing open the door and entering slowly. "And how is the Gentle Doctor today?"

"I don't know why you call me that," he answered with a touch of asperity.

Nurse Ozaki had paused at the door. "I do," she said softly and slipped outside.

Mr. Tayama flopped onto a wooden stool, at once relaxing his large body. "Any good news about my little Toyo this morning?" he asked. His 10-year-old daughter had been hospitalized there for the last three weeks with a slight case of TB.

"Much better. We were able to get hold of some fresh vegetables and I think the new diet is helping greatly."

"I'm glad to hear that." The other man paused. "Do you have a minute to chat?"

"Always with you," Dr. Sakurai said instantly and meant it. Engineer Tayama, with the research section of the Mitsubishi Arms Manufacturing Plant, often had interesting stories to relate, and always seemed eager to enlighten his doctor friend with some new aspect of scientific development. The two men had become close friends in the past few months.

"Did you hear about the terrible new bomb at Hiroshima?" he asked now.

"Only what the newspapers said, something about a 'new-type' weapon."

Mr. Tayama's mouth tightened. "I know a little more, and I can tell you that it looks bad, very bad, I'm afraid."

He didn't have to expand his statement. The two men had talked often before and both had despaired over the future of the Empire. Both believed that continuation of the war was now utter folly, though neither had actually put it into so many words.

"How much damage did the bomb do?" the doctor asked.

"I've heard that it caused terrible damage and death. I wonder. Such power surely cannot be the result of any chemical energy."

"Then what can it be?" Dr. Sakurai asked anxiously. Although patients were waiting outside, he wanted very much to know the answer to that question.

"The Hiroshima-type bomb could not have been exploded by the chemical dissolution of a nitrogenous compound, like nitroglycerin, no matter how much of it had been accumulated," his friend explained, with his disconcerting habit of launching into overly technical terms. "It must be some new kind of energy."

"Could it possibly be atomic energy?" the doctor asked. He wasn't sure he even knew what the phrase meant, but he had read something about it recently.

"That's what I've been told the American President just announced," Mr. Tayama whispered.

"What? Are you sure?"

The other nodded. "I have it on good authority. He said that the 'powers of the sun had been harnessed.' "

"What on earth does that mean? How does it affect people?"

"I don't know. But I think . . ."

He stopped as the air-raid siren sounded. Mr. Tayama sighed and stood up. "Well, here comes Mr. Enemy, right on schedule." Dr. Sakurai also rose, considering what he should do. His orders were to evacuate all patients and hospital personnel to the dugouts. Still, they had all become so used to the air raids and to the fact that usually there was no great threat to them that he was inclined to spare the patients the discomfort of moving. Besides, it would soon be mealtime. Months ago, he had had to reduce the number of hospital meals—mostly rice, plus whatever else was available—from three a day to two, and patients on the third floor were soon to be served "brunch." Today it was to be rice and a thick vegetable soup.

Dr. Sakurai decided to have a look outside for himself. He and Mr. Tayama walked out the door and stood looking upward for a few seconds. The sky was clear, blue—and empty.

"Looks like a false alarm today," said Mr. Tayama. "But I should be getting back anyhow."

"See you again soon," said the doctor. After the other man had gone, Dr. Sakurai continued to look up at the sky. Was that a single plane he saw, high in the sky? He stared but the bright sky made his eyes water. Probably not. He had spotted B-29s on other occasions and had warned the patients not to stick their heads out of the windows in case of attack. Planes, presumably from U. S. aircraft carriers, had twice passed low over his hospital, but no shots had yet been fired.

Sweating now beneath the hot sun, Dr. Sakurai turned and made his way back to the office. "All quiet on the western front," he said lightly to Nurse Ozaki and was rewarded by one of her smiles. He thought he had better look in on Dr. Miyazaki, and walked down the hall to the examination room. Pushing open the door, he saw the doctor giving pneumothorax treatment to a patient. He waited until she had withdrawn the long needle from the patient's side, then said, "Dr. Miyazaki, you really should put that off during an air-raid alarm."

She turned and he saw the deep circles beneath her eyes. "But so many are still waiting," she replied with concern.

And Dr. Sakurai thought: How very like her to answer that way. She is so thoughtful of others, so uncaring of herself. She was a small woman, thin, about 30 years old, and not possessed of a robust constitution. Yet every morning she walked through the mountain pass, a distance of nearly three miles, to come to the hospital and help care for these sick people. It must be taking its toll, for she appeared very tired indeed.

"Won't you rest awhile?" he said gently. "I'll take over."

"How kind of you," she said. "I am a little tired this morning. I think I will rest for a while." She walked slowly out of the room, heading for her upstairs office.

Dr. Sakurai, assisted by Nurse Ozaki, started to treat the patients just as the all-clear sounded. At that moment, Father Kawamoto stuck his head in the door. "Confessions begin in half an hour," he said. "Will you please inform the patients?"

Dr. Sakurai nodded. Father Kawamoto, gruff and gray-haired, had been listening to the confessions of the Catholics every day that summer in the hospital chapel. Now, with Assumption Day only a week away there was an endless row of people waiting to confess and perhaps to pray for an end to the killing. Dr. Sakurai hoped that their prayers would be successful. Then all at once he remembered Mr. Tayama's words . . . "the powers of the sun had been harnessed. . . ." What did it mean?

0840 HOURS

CHUCK SWEENEY WAS BEGINNING TO FEEL AS IF HE HAD WALKED in front of a pack of black cats and under a dozen ladders that morning. First, it had been the trapped fuel, then the black box episode, and now something else had gone wrong. Half an hour ago, he had reached the rendezvous point over Yakashima Island. He had been at 31,000 feet and he had been able to see far below him a Super Dumbo (B-29) and a Dumbo Catalina flying in a wide circle as two submarines floated lazily on the water. They were part of the air-sea rescue operation and were there to pick up Sweeney and his crew if they were forced to ditch.

That possibility had been growing stronger by the minute. The fuel problem was looming ever larger. Two minutes after Sweeney had reached the rendezvous point, Captain Bock's plane had glided up alongside and Bock had waggled his wings in greeting. But for the past thirty minutes there had been absolutely no sign of the third plane flown by Major Hopkins.*

Now Sweeney turned to Don Albury sitting beside him. "Where the hell is Hoppy?" he snapped in exasperation. Radio silence from the strike force had to be maintained at all costs, so he could not reach Hopkins that way. Sweeney was in a quandary. His orders had been to wait no longer than fifteen minutes at rendezvous before proceeding to target. But Sweeney desperately wanted the mission to be a complete success, and it would hardly be called that if no photographs were taken of the explosion. He had no way

* There were two small islands east of Yakashima. Major Hopkins had apparently zeroed in on the larger of the two and had also been circling, trying in vain to spot the other two planes.

of knowing that Dr. Serber, the photo expert, was not even on Hopkins' plane.

In the rear of the plane, Jake Beser continued to watch his small electronic console and to listen to the voice communications. So far, it seemed to be only routine Japanese messages, which was good news. It meant that the Japanese militarists had not grasped the implications of Hiroshima. If they had, special instructions would have been issued and enemy fighters would even now be lying in wait for two- or three-plane bomber formations, to insure that another such bomb would not reach target. But, so far at least, this small group had apparently been ignored.

Beside him, Radioman Spitzer had earphones clamped to his head, just in case there should be additional "friendly" messages. But he doubted it. Some twenty-five minutes ago, he had received a coded message from the weather plane at Kokura stating that the sky was clear and cloudless over the primary target. Shortly thereafter, the weather plane from Nagasaki came in to report the conditions over the secondary target: "Hazy, two-tenths cloud coverage, clearing rapidly." It seemed that both cities were suitable targets.

A few feet away, seated at the scanner window, Sergeant Ray Gallagher from Chicago was trying hard not to think about the bomb just in back of him. At Tinian, when the selected crews had been shown pictures of the test A-bomb explosion at Alamogordo, Gallagher had been deeply disturbed. Secretly, he half-believed that no plane dropping such a bomb could possibly survive the explosion, and Hiroshima had only partially alleviated his fears. He wondered really if any of them would return from this flight. Instinctively, he glanced to the right of the window where a rag doll of indeterminate sex hung on a metal hook. That doll, a present from his niece, had accompanied him on every mission he had flown. It was his good-luck piece, a charm that, so far, had never failed him.

Another Chicago boy, Second Lieutenant Fred Olivi, at 22 the youngest man on board, was also thinking about dropping the bomb. He had sorted it all out in his mind and come up with the conclusion that they had been chosen for this vital mission and it was up to them to carry it off to the best of their ability. He was convinced that if the enemy had the bomb, they would not hesitate to use it. All he and the others could do was to accomplish their mission and hope it would finish things quickly.

But he was worried because at the moment the success of that mission was in jeopardy. As a pilot, he knew that at this altitude they were pulling a lot of power and consuming a great deal of fuel. It was fast becoming a critical situation and he was beginning to wonder why Major Sweeney continued to wait. He reasoned that he, much younger than the major, did not have the skipper's overall knowledge of the mission. Still, he wished they would get on with it.

Navigator Jimmy Van Pelt had been informed of the weather reports on both targets. Although he had already charted the routes to both Nagasaki and Kokura, he did it one more time. Then, just to be on the safe side, he charted a course from Kokura to Nagasaki—the fastest, most direct one. He knew that if for some reason they had to go on to Nagasaki, they would need to get there in a great hurry.

Forty-five minutes after reaching the rendezvous, Chuck Sweeney made up his mind. "The hell with it," he said to Albury. "We can't wait any longer." He dipped his wings at Bock's plane and wheeled over the shore of the mainland. In Kokura, some 400,000 people were blissfully unaware of the two B-29s now heading in their direction. And in Nagasaki, only a handful of people noticed that the wind had just changed. It was now blowing steadily in from the China Sea, driving a weather front before it.

CHAPTER 5

The Warning

0840 HOURS

From the diary of Professor Shirabe of the Nagasaki Medical College:

THE AIR-RAID ALARM WAS LIFTED JUST IN TIME FOR ME TO TEACH MY NINE O'CLOCK CLASS. THE DAYS ARE SO HECTIC NOW WHAT WITH THE ACCELERATED PROGRAM OF TRYING TO COMPRESS FOUR YEARS' WORK INTO THREE. ALSO, AS MORE AND MORE INTERNS AND RESIDENTS ARE CALLED INTO SERVICE, THE BURDENS OF TEACHING AND CLINICAL WORK INCREASE GREATLY FOR THOSE OF US LEFT HERE. STILL, I SUPPOSE WE ARE LUCKY NOT TO HAVE TO FACE THE DANGERS OF BATTLE.

AFTER MY CLASS, I ATTENDED A BRIEF MEETING OF SENIOR FACULTY MEMBERS. EVER SINCE THE HOSPITAL AND COLLEGE BUILDINGS WERE BOMBED ON AUGUST 1, WE HAVE ALL AGREED THAT SOMETHING SHOULD BE DONE TO INDICATE TO ENEMY AIRCRAFT THAT A HOSPITAL IS ON OUR CAMPUS. NOW, A DECISION HAS BEEN REACHED: ON THE ROOFS OF ALL THE BUILDINGS WILL BE PAINTED A GIANT RED CROSS. THE PAINTING WILL START TOMORROW, AUGUST 10.

SUMAKO FUKUDA, FIXING BREAKFAST IN HER HOME JUST BELOW the University Hospital, was easier in her mind than she had been for some time. Remembering the conference in her house last night, she was very glad that she had been able to persuade her parents to leave. Even though she herself had survived the night—a fact which surprised her—she was still convinced that they were all in grave danger here in the city.

Last evening, she had arrived home from her job as an accountant at the teachers' college only to find the entrance filled with *getas* (wooden clogs). When she entered the living room, she discovered a large group of people—mostly neighbors—talking with solemn faces.

Sumako, 23 and full of warm humor, said brightly: "Am I intruding on a top-secret conference?"

Her father looked up and did not return her smile. "Yes, this is a secret conference. We are discussing what to do about—*this*." With that he pulled out a large piece of paper from under the cushion he was sitting on, and gave it to her. She saw that it was a leaflet with writing and drawing on it. But the first thing that struck her was the quality of the paper—snow-white and very good in texture. Japanese paper then in use was cheap and coarse.

"Where did this come from?" she asked.

"Mrs. Yamada brought it," her father answered, pointing to the middle-aged woman on his right, a good friend and next-door neighbor. It seemed that Mrs. Yamada had been visiting a farm out in the country. Someone in the farm family had discovered a whole packet of leaflets in the field and given one to her. Mrs. Yamada assumed that it had been dropped by American planes since the message clearly was a warning to the citizens of Nagasaki to leave their city before it was too late. She had brought it to Mr. Fukuda who was the vice-chairman of the neighborhood association.

Sumako was still studying the leaflet. Alongside the printed message in Japanese was a picture of a clock with dates, and August 8 was circled.

"Well, what do you think?" her father asked impatiently.

That particular date—August 8—had registered at once with her. The war had started on December 8 (Japanese time), and she reasoned that the eighth of the month had to be an important day to both Japan and America. Therefore, she thought it likely that a big air raid might come on that day. "I have a feeling that it might happen tonight," she said at last.

There was silence for a moment and Sumako began to wonder if she should have said anything. The military had been in strict control for so long that people were afraid to speak of what was on their minds. Still, in the privacy of their own homes and among trusted friends, they were inclined to be less cautious. So it was that now they nodded and said almost in chorus that they agreed with her. "Tonight the blow will fall," was the consensus.

"But what can we do about it?" Mrs. Yamada asked plaintively.

Sumako asked her father for permission to speak and when he nodded, she quickly suggested that all dependents—elderly people, children and invalids—should be evacuated from the city. Sumako had many supporters for her idea who agreed to act immediately. But they would not report it to the police, for then they might be accused of spreading an "unpatriotic" rumor—a dangerous charge. And they tacitly agreed that whatever course of action individuals chose—either to flee or to stay—would be strictly up to each person.

After the neighbors dispersed, the Fukuda family had started supper. The idea of an imminent air raid seemed increasingly disturbing to Sumako's mother and she proposed that they all pull out to a friendly farmer's house in the country. But Sumako protested. "You can't leave the house empty. Mother and Father, you both go. I'll stay."

Her father had recently broken two ribs in a fall and had to use a cane to get about. Still, he felt that he, as a leader of the community and the one in charge of vegetable rationing, must live up to his responsibility. Moreover, it was out of the question to think of leaving his young daughter alone in the house. But when Sumako's sister said that she would stay too, Sumako insisted that her parents go that night, pointing out that they could always return later the next day. They finally gave in.

After their parents had left, the two young girls began to grow uneasy, and Sumako's sister suggested they spend the night with Mrs. Yamada and her daughter. That evening the women chatted well into the night. Always their conversation returned to the possibility of a large air raid that night, and even after they had retired, their ears were constantly cocked for the sound of bombers.

The next morning Sumako was boiling rice for breakfast when her mother entered the house. "What are you doing back here so early?" Sumako asked.

"I forgot to tell you girls where I keep the mosquito nets. I was afraid you wouldn't be able to sleep without them, so I told your father to rest and that I would come back alone."

"You shouldn't have bothered. We slept with the Yamadas."

This brought up the subject of the dire predictions of the night before, and they congratulated each other that there had been no raid during the night. Sumako said that they better all have some food before the regular mail (the daily U. S. air raid to Omura) came. Sumako wakened her older sister and the three had breakfast. Then Mrs. Fukuda said, "You better get ready to go to work, Sumako."

"Oh, do I have to? I don't feel well. I have a headache."

"Nonsense, my girl. This is a national emergency. Everybody is working. You can't just take a day off when you feel like it."

"But, Mother—"

"No, no more talk. Go get ready. Mother will fix you something special for dinner tonight."

"All right." She went upstairs, leaving the job of washing the dishes to her sister, and put on her *mompe* and a light-blue cotton blouse. Then she checked her first-aid kit in which she kept a jar of mentholatum, a small bottle of Mercurochrome, a little gauze and two cakes of soap.

Sumako opened the shutters and looked outside. The skies had grown overcast. There was little breeze, and the cicadas were already beginning to sing thickly. To all appearances, it could have been any peaceful day, at any time. War seemed very remote. As she looked down, she saw several hens scratching the ground for food. They didn't seem worried. Maybe everything will be all right after all, she thought wistfully.

Riding his bicycle, Toshiaki Taneguchi, 18, was delivering letters in his district, the area between Ohashi and Michinoo. He had been doing the same thing for the last two years, ever since his graduation from primary school, and now he was wondering how much longer he would be a mailman. There was a possibility that he might be called up for service, but he doubted it. Mail delivery in those days was high priority, and unless things got very much worse for Japan, he supposed that he would continue to be deferred.

That morning he had arisen at seven o'clock. He had spent the night at the post office, as he had been accustomed to doing lately, since it was a lengthy and tiring trip with no bus service from his house at the foot of Mt. Inasa to the post office in the heart of the Urakami Valley. Even if he was at home when an air-raid alarm sounded, he was required to return at once to the post office to guard it against damage.

Soon after he had dressed and put on his gaiters and protective helmet, his grandmother had brought him his breakfast and lunch from home. His family was engaged in farming and chicken-raising, and they were therefore most fortunate in the matter of having enough food.

Carrying the bags of mail, Taneguchi pedaled away from the post office at about nine. Since the women's dormitory of the Mitsubishi Arms Manufacturing Plant was on his beat, there was plenty of mail. He had made certain observations in the course of his career. One was that women received much more mail than men.

Shortly before he reached the police post at Nishi-Urakami, his bicycle began to wobble drunkenly, and when he looked down he saw that he had a flat tire. On duty at the police post was a familiar figure and Taneguchi greeted him as he leaned his bicycle against the wooden structure.

"Good morning," the policeman replied. "What brings you here?"

"I'm afraid my bicycle's got a flat tire. Is there an extra bike here that you can let me use?"

"I'm sorry but ours are broken, too."

As Taneguchi stood wondering what next to do, the policeman suddenly asked: "What do you think about the new-type bomb used at Hiroshima?"

"I don't know," he said absently, as he set out once more pushing his bicycle and delivering the letters. Maybe he could replace the bike at the Nishi-Urakami post office. What had the policeman meant? He had not wanted to show his ignorance, but the other man's words had not meant anything to him. The truth was that he knew nothing whatsoever about any new-type bomb. He promptly forgot about it.

0950 HOURS

IT WAS INTENSELY HOT BY NOW IN NAGASAKI, AND PEOPLE mopped their brows and fanned themselves in the warm stickiness. Chuck Sweeney, on board *Bock's Car,* was beginning to sweat, too. Things were still going wrong for him. Navigator Jimmy Van Pelt had brought them straight as an arrow to Kokura, but once there Sweeney was dismayed to see that the "clear skies" reported by the weather plane were now filled with broken clouds. Since their orders were to bomb only visually, he wondered if Bombardier Beahan would be able to get a fix.

He called ahead to Beahan. "What do you think, Bea?"

Beahan had already clamped his eye to the rubber eyepiece of the Norden MK 15 bombsight, trying to spot familiar landmarks. Now, as a river with recognizable configurations came into the sights between the clouds, he called back, "Shouldn't be any trouble, Chuck."

Sweeney pressed the bomb-run button and as the bomb-bay doors slowly swung open, a steady hum filled the plane. That hum would stop only when the bomb had been dropped or the doors closed again.

The members of the crew had already begun to put on the special purple-lens protective goggles. Only Beahan had left his off. He was having enough trouble as it was trying to find the aiming point: The Kokura arsenal, which even at that moment was in the process of turning out both light and heavy weapons for Japan's fighting men. Now the railroad yard came under the cross hairs. Good! That meant that the arsenal was only a mile away.

Suddenly, everything on the ground was blotted out by a layer of dark gray smoke. "Damn it!" he muttered. "Damn it to hell!"

Sweeney heard him. "What's the matter?"

"The aiming point is obscured by smoke. Seems to be coming from a nearby factory." It was indeed. Two days earlier, the Yawata steel factory had been conventionally bombed. It was still burning, and the strong east wind was blowing the smoke directly over that part of Kokura.

They were nearing the end of the bomb run. "I can't see it," Beahan cried at last. "We'll have to make another run."

Sweeney flipped on the intercom button. "Pilot to crew: No drop," he said. "Repeat, no drop." He jerked the wheel sharply to the left and the plane began to turn. "Bea, we'll make a full sweep and come in again."

"Roger."

Minutes later, they were thundering in on the city on their prescribed course.

"There's flak coming up," Beahan cried, spotting the puffs through the bombsight. "Right on us, but not up here yet."

Flak! Just what they needed, thought Sweeney. But if Beahan said that flak was near, it was near. Beahan had been shot down four times in Europe, and he knew what he was talking about.

Now "Pappy" Dehart in the tail-gun bubble confirmed it. "Flak!" he yelled. "It's wide but altitude is perfect."

"Roger, Pappy," said Sweeney.

"Major, the flak is coming closer."

"Roger."

"Major!" His voice had risen in his excitement. Now it sounded like a squeak. "Major, this damn flak is right on our tail and coming closer all the time."

"Forget it, Pappy," Sweeney snapped. "We're on a bomb run."

Jake Beser, watching his radio screen and listening, had begun to pick up signals near the Japanese fighter control frequencies. He could recognize the differences between ground and airborne signals and these were definitely airborne and getting stronger.

Once more, Beahan was squinting into the rubber eyepiece. One after another, he saw a stadium, a cathedral, the same river—then the thick smoke again blanketed the ground. "I can't pick up the aiming point," he growled.

Sweeney gritted his teeth and as they passed over the edge of the city, he shoved the wheel and said again, "No drop. Repeat. No drop."

Sergeant Ed Buckley at the other scanner window broke in

excitedly, "Skipper, Jap Zeros are coming up at us. Looks like about ten."

"Roger." Sweeney was not worried about the Zeros. He very much doubted if they would be able to climb to this great altitude. But the flak bothered him. He remembered from the briefing that Kokura, the "Pittsburgh of Japan," was one of the most heavily defended areas in the whole Empire. He decided to climb another thousand feet in hopes of confusing the Japanese gunners.

Minutes later, he said, "Bea, let's come in from the east."

"Roger."

Sweeney turned to Ashworth who was now standing between him and Albury. "We'll try one more run," he said. "This time, we'll come in from another angle."

Ashworth nodded, wondering for a moment what would happen if a flak burst caught them.

"Coming in from the east, Bea," Sweeney said calmly.

"Roger."

But once again, the aiming point was not visible, and at the end of the run, Sweeney asked Ashworth, "We have to bomb visually, don't we?" As joint commanders, the two men had to agree on every important decision.

"Those are my orders," Ashworth said, looking at Sweeney with a set expression.

The plane was beginning to jump now from the closer flak bursts. Ray Gallagher, watching the puffs outside his window, began to mutter in his intercom, "Let's move. Let's get the hell out of here." Abe Spitzer was mumbling, "What's wrong with Nagasaki? What about Nagasaki?" Sweeney finally told them to "knock off the chatter."

Then Sergeant Kuharek came on, sounding worried. "Skipper, fuel is getting critical. We have just about enough now to get us back to Iwo."

"Roger." Iwo be damned, he thought. He was not about to return with the bomb still on board. That bomb was damn well going to be dropped if he had anything to say about it. He turned to Ashworth, his co-commander. "We'll go on to secondary target, if you agree."

Ashworth nodded again. "The only choice. Let's hope the weather is better there."

"Proceeding to Nagasaki," Sweeney announced to the crew as he swung the plane in a steep-banked turn. Behind him, Captain Bock in *The Great Artiste* had drawn closer to the strike plane. Reporter William Laurence, who had seen the flak getting closer and closer, handed his notebook to the radio operator and said, "Son, if you get back, give this to the first officer you see and say, 'This is the last story Bill Laurence ever wrote.' "

When Sweeney made his sudden turn Bock was caught by surprise. He had been flying behind Sweeney's right wing, but by the time he had reacted to the maneuver and made the turn himself, he was behind the left wing.

Sweeney glanced automatically over his right shoulder to make sure that Bock's plane was following. When he failed to spot *The Great Artiste* in its proper spot, he made a mistake that many other combat pilots have made. Frustrated, preoccupied and more than a little exasperated, he pressed the transmit button instead of the intercom and said clearly, "Where's Bock?"

Amidst strict radio silence, those two words jumped out over the Japanese Empire. Two words, in English, meaningless, yet they could pinpoint a position or imply an unusual enemy operation. Japanese monitors probably heard the words, but evidently no one grasped their significance. Sweeney himself first realized what he had done when Major Jim Hopkins, still circling the rendezvous point hundreds of miles to the south, said excitedly into Sweeney's earphones, "Chuck? Is that you, Chuck? Where the hell are you?"

After the first horrified second, Sweeney clamped his lips shut, angry at himself. What a stupid damn thing to do! Why not just announce your flight plan? It was useless in any case. It was far too late and risky to answer Hopkins now. He sighed heavily, and said softly to Van Pelt, "Jimmy, chart the fastest course to secondary target."

"Already done, Skipper." He recited the exact figures. "But that course will take us right over the Kyushu fighter fields."

"Can't be helped." He made the minor adjustments to put the plane on the right course. They were already an hour and a half behind schedule and the bomb still rode with them, fat and menacing.

Sweeney turned to Albury and shook his head. "Can any other goddamned thing go wrong?"

In Nagasaki, the weather front pushing in from the East China Sea was just touching the outskirts of that city, and thin clouds had already covered the top of Mt. Inasa.

CHAPTER 6

Zero Minus Sixty Minutes

1000 HOURS

THE MOMENT THAT SWEENEY TURNED TOWARD NAGASAKI, 21-year-old Tsuneo Tomita paused to rest. Even as *Bock's Car* had been winging toward the Empire, Tomita, a third-year pharmaceutical student at the Nagasaki Medical College, had been deep inside a dugout shelter swinging a pick. Just last week, he and his fellow students had been ordered to enlarge and extend the existing shelters, and Tomita, dressed only in shorts, was now sweating profusely at that task. He grinned ruefully as he began to swing the pick again. It was a most unprofessional sort of job—for a medical student, at least. Still, he couldn't complain. More than 90 percent of young men his age were off fighting the enemy.

It had been an exhausting summer, nonetheless. On the first of July, the faculty had decided to call off some of the lectures (but not the reading) for all third-year students in the pharmacology section and to use that manpower to construct more shelters. With the first- and second-year students already at work in factories elsewhere in the city, the college had taken on the usual midsummer half-deserted appearance of colleges anywhere. The only ones left on campus were part of the staff, the third- and fourth-year students in the various departments, and a dozen or so ailing lower classmen—barely 700 out of the usual 2000-plus.

Even the atmosphere of the place had changed—and for the worse. When Tomita had first entered the college, the gardens in the center of the campus grounds, surrounded by well-tended lawns, were spectacularly beautiful. They provided an oasis for the students, worn out by the twelve- and thirteen-hour-a-day crash study and work program. Every chance the students had during their jam-packed days and nights, they would lie on the lawns near the gardens, talking, reading, or just sleeping. But by August, with no one to tend them, the gardens had been taken over completely by the weeds. What was even worse, large sections of the lawns had been ripped up to make way for the much-needed sweet-potato patches.

The one compensation to it all was the even closer welding of friendships. A majority of the students, unlike Tomita, had come to the medical college from places outside of Nagasaki, and many of them, with no family to go home to each night, had banded together in close-knit groups, finding in each other the reassurance and warmth they could find nowhere else. Gregarious Tomita, even with a family in town, was caught up in the camaraderie and had his own circle of friends. They were young men who liked each other and the same things.

Late in July, the class program for third-year students had been abandoned. They were expected to continue studying at night, but during the day they did only manual labor. The physical chore of digging in the ground from early morning to late afternoon gave them nothing to occupy their minds. But, like clowns who have forgotten to laugh, they continued their dull work, smeared with sweat and dirt, with few words on their lips, dismayed at the increasing loneliness many of them were beginning to experience. Every day, from Tomita's class, one of his colleagues disregarded his exempt status and left abruptly to be an army cadet or a reserve ensign in the navy. Under air-raid conditions, wild farewell parties were held for the departing student, always with a facade of good cheer, but invariably with an undercurrent of defeat. Since the spring, Japanese cities had been under constant attack, and many had been destroyed. The resulting tension and fear were now taking their toll.

Nagasaki was one of the few cities that remained comparatively unscathed until the last. It was as late as August 1 that the city had suffered its first raids by carrier-borne aircraft. That morning, when Tomita had heard the siren, he and his friend Suenaga, also a Nagasaki resident, had raced to a nearby hillside to get a good view if an attack were made. They had stood watching on the rise, until, like giant silver bats, seven low-flying American planes appeared over the top of Mt. Anakobo and roared toward the university complex. After dropping some gray objects near the hospital and medical school, they zoomed off into the distance. But at that instant, two of the buildings were engulfed by fire and smoke.

Instinctively, Tomita had thrown himself headfirst into the weeds. The war had at last come to him personally. He did not like the experience.

"Are you all right, Tomita?" his friend, also face down, had called.

"Yes. And you? The planes were very low."

"Come," Suenaga said impatiently. "We must not hide here and tremble."

And, rising quickly, the two young men had run through the grove of camphor trees down to the college shelter.

Chemistry Professor Sugiura had greeted them with anger. "What's the idea of entering the shelter at this time? Don't you realize that coming here during an air raid might allow the enemy to spot where it is? Didn't you give any thought to the lives of the others here?"

The young men had no answer. They knew the professor was right. From that day on, work on the shelters was intensified, and the students were ordered to be on duty at the college day *and* night.

Getting a good night's sleep at the college was difficult, mainly because of the mosquitoes. Tomita grew accustomed to sleeping on a sofa in the large laboratory, where the powerful smell of chemicals kept the insects away. Many of his classmates slept on the high platforms in the classrooms, which also seemed to be off-limits to the pesky, low-flying mosquitoes.

Early on Wednesday, the eighth of August, Dean Tsunoo, who had witnessed the Hiroshima bomb on his way back from Tokyo, called together the faculty and the students in the auditorium and told them what the Hiroshima bomb had been like and what they could expect should Nagasaki be subjected to the same kind of weapon. Tomita and his friends, unable to grasp the full power of the new bomb, did not pay much heed to the dean's words. They undoubtedly would have been more attentive had they known that the dean, having survived the bomb at Hiroshima, had come back to Nagasaki only to die there.

But when evening drew near, they forgot Dean Tsunoo's remarks as they sprawled on one of the few remaining patches of grass, gazing at the Urakami Cathedral through the plants and weeds of the garden. The students from out of town were enchanted by this famous old cathedral and never tired of looking at it. Even Tomita, who had seen it for many years, still found it a beautiful sight, with its red brick walls, colonnades and inspiring stone statues. All through the day, the bell, sounding from its high tower of bricks, had been summoning the faithful in the valley to pre-Feast-of-Assumption confessions. But somehow, the bell was no longer a source of enduring comfort. Instead, it had begun to sound somewhat plaintive as the war turned more and more against Japan. Even the hills overlooking the cathedral were now covered with the creeping vines of sweet potatoes, and each day through those same hills one could glimpse long funeral processions, the women with white silken veils, winding slowly along, the chant of a Catholic litany or a Buddhist sutra rising from the column.

That evening, lying on the lawn, the young men watched the sun as it neared the top of Mt. Inasa in the west. At that level, it shone through the mountain range and focused on the cross atop the cathedral, twinkling gold at intervals. One of Tomita's friends remarked that it looked like a single beacon in an atmosphere of gloom and melancholy, and the others quietly agreed.

Later, Tomita and two friends, Narasaki and Tada, went to the home of Suenaga where they spent the evening talking and drinking "medicinal sake." It was one of the few occasions during that period that Tomita looked back on with pleasure. The only jarring note occurred when his friend Tada had said unexpectedly: "I don't know why, but I have a hunch I'll die tomorrow."

They all tried to tease him out of his melancholy state, but he was steadfast in his presentiment. "I know it doesn't make any sense," he said, shaking his head slowly, "but I know it somehow. I will die."

That night, Tomita and his friends slept together in the college building for the last time.

Reporter Junji Sato of the Nagasaki branch of the Domei News Bureau had no thought of dying. Things were bad, he knew, but he was also convinced that some event would soon resolve the indecision that seemed to plague the leaders of his country. Sato was one of the few well-informed people in Nagasaki that day. In fact, he had known for three days the sequence of events that now indicated a bleak future for the Empire.

It had all begun on the afternoon of August 7. On that Tuesday, the members of the Domei News Bureau, ten people in all, had been enjoying their customary afternoon break between morning and evening news transmissions, when the communications operator suddenly interrupted their idle conversations. "Attention, everybody," she exclaimed, clutching at the earphones on her head. "Attention! There will be an important announcement from Imperial Headquarters in exactly one minute."

The entire staff froze at her words. Reporter Sato, startled at first, soon began to speculate on what this news might portend. An Imperial Headquarters announcement was rare and always unexpected. At the beginning of the war, such statements had been eagerly awaited, for they invariably signaled a dramatic Japanese victory of some sort. But now, under the present bleak war conditions, an announcement from headquarters usually meant bad news, perhaps the death of an important personality, or a major defeat, or even news of an enemy landing on the shores of the main islands.

Rewriteman Sugita jumped for a nearby telephone and, flipping a switch to cut into the special line, listened intently. At the end of a minute his knuckles began to whiten as he gripped the telephone, and everyone knew that the announcement had begun. Sugita's face was not a gambler's face, for it reflected his every emotion. Now, in the space of a few seconds, his expression changed from dread, to astonishment, finally to utter bewilderment. Putting down the phone, he turned to the others.

"What was the announcement, Sugita-san?" someone cried. "Tell us what has happened."

Sugita nodded his head slowly, his brows still drawn together in wonder. "It was a strange announcement," he said softly. "Imperial Headquarters has just reported that Hiroshima was raided yesterday, the sixth of August, by a small number of American B-29s and that the city incurred fairly heavy damage. Moreover, it appears that the enemy used a new type of bomb during the raid, but details of that are still under investigation."

There was a chorus of "ahs" at his words and the people in the room exchanged looks ranging from relief to puzzlement. Reporter Sato's mind had already moved into high gear, searching for the meaning between the lines of the terse message. Sato was only 26, but already he had established a reputation as a balanced, rational individual. While Sugita was emotional, Sato was analytical. Sugita reacted impulsively, while the wiry, lantern-jawed Sato chose to reason things out, to reach a carefully deliberated conclusion. He prided himself on his self-control under trying circumstances. He did not guess that he was soon to be thoroughly tested for the first time in his life.

At that moment, he merely let Sugita's words sift into possible patterns of interpretation. In all of their previous announcements, the military had consistently understated the adverse aspect of situations. When, for example, they reported that certain army units were presently "engaged in hot fighting," it more often meant that the home position had already been occupied by the enemy and that the Japanese forces had probably either been killed or captured. The military also used the words "strategic transfer" for "withdrawal," and when the enemy had overrun a Japanese position, the defenders were said to be engaged in a "circling maneuver to attack the enemy from the rear." Even air raids caused only "insignificant damage" and the Japanese people were invariably told that the enemy planes had been "completely routed" and even then were "being destroyed by the invincible Japanese defenders of the sky." Therefore, Sato realized that the latest Imperial Headquarters admission that damages had been "fairly heavy" could only mean that the "new-type bomb" had been extremely powerful.

It was bad news without a doubt, probably the worst since he had been with the Domei News Bureau. Not that it had been a bad year in other respects. In fact, he considered himself most fortunate to be where he was at the time, exempt from the service and living in what might be considered "privileged circumstances." In the summer of 1944, the aged Torao Yamanobe, head of the venerable and wealthy Yamanobe family, had offered the Nagasaki bureau a room in his lavish European-style home, saying that the residence was too big for an old couple to take care of in the tense and unsettling war situation. The bureau had quickly accepted this splendid offer and had converted the room into a comfortable office. It was a spacious room, with windows on three sides providing more than enough light for the staff to work. In the summertime, cool winds blew the heat out of the room, and in winter the sunlight streaming through the six-foot-high windows turned the room into a veritable sunporch. Early in 1945, the aged Yamanobe couple withdrew to the country, leaving everything in charge of the Domei people. Thus, the entire two-story reddish-brick mansion became theirs—almost a paradise for those who worked there.

There was never any problem in getting the staff to show up for work, for it usually meant exchanging cramped living quarters for relative luxury. Even during night air raids, the day workers preferred to leave their homes and seek the sanctuary of the office rather than the hot, airless shelters. With the office manned night and day by two shifts of workers, the bureau was in constant touch, via military telephone, with the Nagasaki Fortress Command. It also kept open the line to the Fukuoka main office of Domei so that the staffers could keep abreast of both national and local (province) developments.

The staffers themselves were a congenial group consisting of rewritemen, communications operators, stenographers, translators and reporters. In charge was Managing Editor Yamanaka, a stout six-footer, a demanding boss and a heavy drinker. Most people wondered how the ME managed to find so much sake in wartime Japan. Reporter Sato could have told them. He had obtained sake for his boss a number of times. At that time, the so-called privileged classes were the military, the government people, men of influence and black-marketeers. These people never need worry about obtaining sake or tobacco. The press had less prestige than the government people but more than the "men of influence," so they were in a position to buy such rare items at low, official prices merely by presenting a written application.

The Domei News Bureau had two main functions: to serve as a political and military arm of communication, and to disseminate a certain amount of "permissible" news to the people. In effect, a private organization had become a state-policy news propaganda agency. With radio equipment installed at all local branches of Domei, located in every prefectural government capital throughout Japan, the bureau was an invaluable emergency means of keeping in touch in case the nationwide network of government and military communications should be paralyzed by a succession of air raids. Without such a safety valve, telegram messages and vital military orders would have had to be hand-carried by messengers on trains. Even at this point, the value of the Domei network had become evident. With Japanese cities being bombed daily and with the war situation becoming graver by the day, direct communications between the central government in Tokyo and the regional governmental offices had become increasingly difficult. As a result, code telegrams of the government offices had begun to find their way into the Domei channels with growing regularity. Over Domei's leased telephone lines came detailed reports of damages incurred in various cities. Labeled "top-secret information," these were passed back and forth between the dozen or so bureaus, including the Nagasaki branch which, in turn, relayed them to local defense headquarters, the police departments, and specified institutions, such as the Mitsubishi heavy industries complex.

The other half of Domei's function was to let the people in on what was going on in their own country. But getting all of the news to the people was impossible at this losing stage of the game. For one thing, the news was not generally very encouraging, and censorship imposed by the government and the military had become stricter than ever. Even the choice of newspapers available to the people of Nagasaki had been drastically limited. Under the control of the National Board of Information, the four main newspapers in Nagasaki had been merged into one paper, the Nagasaki *Nippo.* The three national dailies—*Asahi, Mainichi* and *Yomiuri*—were no longer circulated in the prefectures a long way from Tokyo, including southernmost Nagasaki prefecture. In their place, the Nagasaki *Nippo* was now delivered to all their former subscribers. Only the *Nishinippon Shimbun* had been given permission to distribute within the prefecture. The local Domei news bureau supplied news and features to both the *Nippo* and *Nishinippon Shimbun.*

What was printed, even how it was printed, was "suggested" by directives from the press division of Imperial Headquarters. Most announcements and articles emanating from headquarters or from one of the regional military commands were accompanied by directives to play up a certain story, handle another one "routinely," give three-column, front-page space to a particular announcement, or "back-page," or play down, any gloomy news.

It turned out that no such directive was attached to the follow-up story of the Hiroshima announcement when it arrived on August 8. It was just after lunch when the bell of the military telephone linking the Nagasaki bureau with the Fortress Command, the local military force, rang. A stenographer took down the story which had originally come from Imperial Headquarters. It stated in part that:

1. The new-type bomb, to which a parachute is attached, explodes with a blinding flash of light in the air, five to six hundred yards above the ground.

2. The skin of a person on the ground exposed to the bomb explosion becomes ulcerated.

3. War lessons to be learned from it are that burns are slight when a person is clad in white, and that more tunnels should be dug for air-raid shelters, since wooden buildings are often smashed flat.

It was a puzzling, somewhat unsatisfying bit of addenda to what the staff already knew. What was even stranger to reporter Sato, however, was the absence of a report on the bomb explosion from the spot where it had taken place, the Hiroshima branch of Domei. The Nagasaki bureau always received detailed reports on the number of houses destroyed, casualties and overall damage from air raids on cities from all the Domei bureaus, but this time no information had been received from Hiroshima, not one word. Sato began to think that this might be the result of very widespread damage. Perhaps the building which housed the news bureau had been one of the ones "smashed flat." He knew that his colleagues in that city would have kept transmitting news as long as the lines were open and they were able to function.

Later in the afternoon, the Nagasaki bureau received a message from the chief of the air defense section of the perfectural government asking that reporters assemble at his office the following morning at eleven. He said that he wanted to publish war lessons obtained from the new-type bomb explosion. He added that they here in Nagasaki would probably never have any need for such lessons, but the readers might be interested anyhow.

That evening, when Sato returned home from the office, his younger sister Teruko was already there, having come back earlier than usual from her work at the Mitsubishi Arms Manufacturing Plant. Teruko, a junior in high school, was also the leader of the Student Patriotic Corps working at that factory. Sato saw that she was energetically making a pair of *mompe*—the best apparel for Japanese women at that time.

Before starting the fire for the evening meal, Sato walked over to his sister. "Teruko, there has been some disturbing news," he said as she looked up at him. "It's about a new type of bomb that the Americans are using. From now on, I want you to enter the underground shelter without fail whenever an air-raid alarm is sounded."

His sister looked at him blankly. "We are not really in any great danger, are we?"

"None at all," he said at once. "Still, there's no harm in being careful. Will you do what I said?"

"Of course," Teruko said brightly.

Teruko had already left the house the next morning when he awoke. Since his mother was staying overnight with a relative, he had to fix his own breakfast, then left quickly for the office. There he found that the day's work schedule was already at rush status. The managing editor spotted him as he walked in and beckoned to him.

"Sato," the big man said, "go over to the steelworks. They have a release for us."

"Right. I'll go at once," he said. But before he could leave, there was a cry from the communications operator who had been taking messages over the line linking the Nagasaki bureau with the Fukuoka regional office.

"The Soviet Union has just entered the war," the operator shouted. "The Russians are now fighting against us."

Managing Editor Yamanaka's expression had turned black. "The cowards!" he muttered. "Even with a treaty, they turn on us. The cowardly wolves hoping to get a bite of the carcass."

Someone yelled at him to take the phone and he picked it up angrily, almost barking into it. Sato stood listening, not knowing whether to leave or not. Judging from Mr. Yamanaka's words, it seemed that something important was being discussed. The managing editor concluded by saying, "Yes, all right. I'll take measures immediately." He hung up, his expression troubled, and turned to his reporter. "Sato, we have been asked to communicate immediately with Tokyo about the Soviet entry. Apparently, the news had not reached Tokyo yet because of the interruption of the lines at Hiroshima. You better go to the wireless station at Isahaya right away and try to get through. Of course, you no longer need go to the steelworks."

Getting to Isahaya, some fifteen miles away, was his immediate concern. Despite his status as a war correspondent, he did not have free access to a car. So he called on Governor Nagano at Defense Headquarters who would be able to provide him with transportation. Once there, he informed the governor of the news of the Soviet entry into the war. At first, the governor was breathless with shock. Then, as the impact sank in, he quietly folded his hands on the table, lowered his head, and began to weep. Sato was dismayed at the sight but did not know what to do. After a while, the governor raised his head and said hoarsely, "The new bomb on Hiroshima has brought the entire venture to an end. On top of it the Soviet Union has joined the war against us. It is now only a matter of time." His head dropped again, and he stared down at his lap.

Sato hesitated, then spoke. Could the governor please

lend him an automobile so that he could inform Tokyo of the developments? When the governor raised his face this time, Sato was surprised to see that he again wore the self-possessed look of an executive.

"Of course I will," he said crisply. "It's an emergency. You can use my car. I'll send it round to your office."

Back at the office, Sato told the managing editor that he had secured transportation to Isahaya and would leave at once. He was waiting downstairs when the car arrived and was just about to climb in when Mr. Yamanaka stuck his head out of the upstairs window and shouted, "Wait a minute, Sato. We've just learned that communications with Tokyo have been reopened. You don't have to go to Isahaya after all. Just stick around and be sure to cover the press conference."

At about ten that morning, new information about the bombing of Hiroshima began to flow in as "top-secret information, not to be passed along to unauthorized personnel under any circumstances." Skimming over the transmissions, Sato noticed such appalling phrases as "the army in Hiroshima was annihilated," "scores of thousands of houses totally destroyed or burned away," and "more than 100,000 dead and at least that many wounded." Sato shuddered. Now he knew that what he had guessed earlier was a fact: This new bomb possessed unimagined destructive power.

A few minutes later, Mr. Yamanaka called Sato over to him. "You know, today is going to be a busy day," he murmured conspiratorially. "On your way to the press conference at the defense chief's office, will you see if you can pick up some sake for me?"

Nodding his head at this not unexpected request, Sato stuck some application forms for special rations of sake in his pocket, walked out of the building, jumped on his bicycle and rode off. He did not have much doubt that he would be able to get the sake for his boss.

He went first to the food section of the prefectural government where he found that most of the officials were in conference. Then he climbed on his bicycle and headed for the building of the taxation office. He began to wonder what excuse he should offer for requesting a special ration of sake at this time. Then he had an idea. I'll mention the Soviet intervention, he thought, and that there is going to be a special editorial conference to discuss it. He almost laughed at the idea. This bureaucratic rigmarole was all so ridiculous.

Just then, he heard the sound of an airplane and he stopped his bicycle and looked up. High above he could see a single silver plane, a tiny dot flitting between the clouds. As he watched, the plane turned sharply and roared back the way it had come. What did that mean? he wondered. His careful analytical mind went to work. Should he head for shelter? He weighed the pros and cons, considering, rejecting, evaluating. At last he came to a conclusion. He had reasoned it out. He was not in any danger here. There was nothing to worry about. He climbed back on his bicycle and pedaled away, whistling with supreme self-confidence.

1050 HOURS

SIX MILES ABOVE NAGASAKI, SWEENEY'S WORST FEARS HAD BEEN realized. There was now a 70 percent cloud cover over the city instead of the 20 percent reported earlier. Beahan, squinting into the eyepiece of the bombsight, was able to make out the outlines of the harbor, the heavily populated downtown section and the mountains surrounding the city. But he doubted that he would be able to spot the aiming point—the Mitsubishi Shipyards in the urban area. He looked up, as clouds once again shut off his vision, and told Sweeney their predicament.

Sweeney had brought *Bock's Car* in from the northeast. The flight from Kokura had been without incident even when they had flown over the Kyushu air base. They were still at 30,000 feet and Chuck Sweeney knew that time was running out. Kuharek had already told him that they had just enough fuel for one run over the target if they expected to reach Okinawa. Even then, he had said, it would be touch and go.

Sweeney's mouth tightened. Hiroshima had come off without a hitch and Tibbets had had enough faith in him to entrust this mission to him. He was damned if he was going to let him down. They could still bring it off. He had asked Ashworth to come forward again. Now he said, "I know our orders are to bomb visually, but we can make only one run and Beahan doesn't think he can get a visual fix. I propose that we drop it by radar. What do you think?"

Ashworth had known the question was coming and had been dreading it.

"I don't know. Let me think about it."

"We haven't got time. We have enough gas for one run. More than that and we'll probably have to ditch before we make Okinawa. And if we don't drop it by radar, we'll have to salvo the bomb in the ocean."

"I just don't know, Chuck." Ashworth's orders had been most explicit. "How accurately can you drop it by radar?"

"I can absolutely guarantee within a thousand feet of designated target," Sweeney answered quickly. "After all, anything is better than dumping it in the water." He took a deep breath. "I have a lot of confidence in my radar and I will take full responsibility."

Van Pelt, hearing this, sucked in his breath. It would be his job to coordinate a radar fix with Buckley. Positioning the bomb-drop had suddenly become his baby.

Ashworth was still wrestling with the dilemma. He considered the possibility of going on to Tokyo, but dismissed it at once. Neither he nor Sweeney could make a decision of that magnitude, even if they had had enough gas. His orders had stated a visual drop only. Still . . .

"OK," he said. "Drop it by radar if you can't find the target visually."

The bomb-bay doors had already opened and the humming had begun, Ray Gallagher fingered his good-luck doll. Jake Beser, monitoring his electronic console, made a last-minute check to make sure all circuits were as programmed. Lieutenant Barnes still stared at the blinking red eye on his black box. Sweeney took the plane in a wide sweep over the harbor and headed north over the center of the city, toward the left-hand valley.

Van Pelt and Buckley had already gone to work. On Van Pelt's radarscope, the city outline appeared round and light blue against the darker blue of the surrounding mountains. Buckley was calling out coastline checkpoints from the radar beams bouncing back, and Beahan was following Van Pelt's course on his bombsight. They all knew they had better get it right. They would only have one chance.

Suddenly, Beahan shouted, "I've got it. I see the city. I'll take it now . . ."

At that very moment, the Japanese leaders of government were in heated debate in Tokyo. Although Hiroshima and the threat posed by the powerful new bomb had shocked them deeply, some of the military leaders even now believed that the country must fight on. Perhaps, now that they had taken the worst that the hated Americans could inflict on them, they could unite the Japanese people into one massive, heroic defense of the Empire. Other leaders, however, urged immediate acceptance of the Potsdam Declaration, providing the integrity of the Emperor was maintained. But the military were adamant. "I am convinced," War Minister Anami had declared, "that the Americans only had one bomb after all."

. . . At Beahan's shout, Sweeney relinquished direction of the plane to his bombardier. Beahan had found a large hole in the clouds some two miles north of the aiming point. He made a two-degree correction, and under the cross hairs he now saw a familiar structure—the Mitsubishi Arms Manufacturing Plant, the secondary target. Without hesitation, he "clutched in" the automatic bombsight mechanism, which in effect selected the instant of release. Seconds later, the wires snapped, the humming stopped, and the plane lurched upward, freed of the great weight.

Grammar forgotten in his excitement, Beahan shouted, "Bombs away!" Sweeney wheeled the plane in the sharp, diving turn they had practiced so often, as the single bomb, in its huge trajectory arc, sank quickly toward the ground. Nagasaki was about to become history.

CHAPTER 7

The Red Circle of Death

1102 HOURS

THERE IS A SPOT IN THE UPPER URAKAMI RIVER WHERE NATURE has formed a small pool. That morning a group of ten boys, in colored loincloths, was playing a game called "find the bell." One of the boys, 11-year-old Koichi Nakajima, had a little gilded bell. He would throw it in the water, count to three and they all would dive after it. The first to find it won the game.

Now Koichi held up the tiny bell and shouted, "Here we go! One, two, three." There were ten splashes as the boys dove for the prize. But the river had become roily, and no one found it.

Koichi began to get worried. He had taken the bell from his sister's workbox without her permission. She would be very angry if he lost it. He surfaced, took a deep breath, and eeled his way down to the bottom.

Nine seconds later, the bomb exploded over his head. When Koichi surfaced, he heard two of the other boys screaming with pain. He stared around in fright. There were bodies of his friends on the riverbank, and beyond them he saw that all the houses had been knocked down. What had been a beautiful city a moment before was now a wasteland with a big, black cloud rising above it like smoke from a funeral pyre. Though it was deathly hot, Koichi's teeth began to chatter.

When the plutonium bomb exploded, fantastic energy was released in the form of heat, light, gamma radiation and pressure. The exact number of people killed will never be known. The prewar census count is meaningless, and because people were constantly moving in and out of cities, no preraid population figure has been determined. Also, many people were burned beyond recognition or were simply obliterated. Finally, hundreds were disposed of in mass cremations, while other hundreds fled to the country and mountains to die unrecorded.

For some 1,000 yards, or three-fifths of a mile, in all directions from the epicenter, within the Red Circle of Death, it was as if a malevolent god had suddenly focused a gigantic blowtorch on a small section of our planet. Within that perimeter, nearly all unprotected living organisms—birds, insects, horses, cats, chickens—perished instantly. Flowers, trees, grass, plants, all shriveled and died. Wood burst into flames. Metal beams and galvanized iron roofs began to bubble, and the soft, gooey masses twisted into grotesque shapes. Stones were pulverized, and for a second every last bit of air was burned away. The people exposed within that doomed section neither knew nor felt anything, and their blackened, unrecognizable forms dropped silently where they stood.

Some people were protected by inevitable yet unpredictable tricks of chance. At the very edge of the Red Circle of Death, a thin and withered old man whose eyesight was fading was on hands and knees behind a three-foot-high stone wall, tenderly weeding around four small sweet potato buds. Behind him stood his wife, criticizing his efforts and offering suggestions as wives do the world over. When the bomb exploded, the old man was barely conscious of the flash, because of the stone wall and his bad eyesight. The first indication he had was that his wife stopped talking in mid-sentence. It was only much later that he was able to understand fully what had taken place. The heat rays emanating from the center of the explosion had swept over the top of the stone wall, well over his head, and had cut down his wife even as she spoke.

Because the radiant heat came in a direct line, shielding behind some sort of object—walls, earth, trees, even leaves—was important. A man writing at his desk was unaffected except for his hands which were badly burned by the rays entering a small window in his house. Generally, the thicker the clothing, the more protection it offered. The rays penetrated a single layer of clothing, and marks of protecting straps, clothing labels, buttons were often clearly visible on the skin. White or light colors provided more protection than darker ones, and bizarre patterns were etched on the flesh of many.

Beyond the Red Circle of Death, fatalities from heat were fewer. But the character of the terrain also had some bearing on the number of deaths. For example, the inhabitants of two blocks 1,500 yards away suffered a disproportionately high mortality rate—because they were situated on the slopes of a valley facing the bomb center, and thus were directly exposed to the explosion. Inversely, another area a bare 1,000 yards from ground zero was not nearly as seriously affected as neighboring areas, because its inhabitants were protected by a steep hill which rose between blast center and their homes.

The kind of shelter involved was another important factor. Within 1,500 yards of ground zero, wooden buildings were inadequate shelter for most. Even reinforced concrete buildings did not protect more than half their inhabitants.

The heat rays, though intense, lasted but a few seconds. Then came the blast. The peculiar topography of Nagasaki confined most of the blast damage to the Urakami Valley. Under the tremendous pressure exerted, a hundred times greater than the strongest typhoon, all buildings within 800 yards of the center were completely destroyed. The blast effects, traveling outward at a speed of 9,000 miles an hour, blew the walls and roofs off houses three miles away. Unlike the heat equation, external injuries were much more frequent among those people who were actually shielded by something. Bamboo poles could splinter and puncture flesh. Collapsing wooden structures could crush and maim. Even in concrete buildings, flying glass and dislodged interior fittings became murderous objects. The swath of destruction that cut through northern Nagasaki in the first few minutes was almost unbelievable. Of the estimated 55,000 buildings in existence at the time, about 20,000 were destroyed either by blast or by fire.

The bomb's probing fingers found their way into the smallest openings, even through tiny high windows in basement rooms. Research Technician Tao had just sat down in his basement laboratory when a great orange light entered the room and bathed the walls in weird shadows and patterns. Mr. Tao leaped toward the chair behind his desk, somehow believing in that split second that he would be better off if he were sitting down. He barely made it and had covered his head with his arms, when it felt as if someone had whacked him across the back with a large, flat board. His breath left his body in a great *Whooosh!* and blackness pulled the curtain down.

Minutes later, when he came to, dazed and bewildered, he was convinced that the prefecture building must have sustained a direct hit. He looked around and saw that he was surrounded by a sea of broken glass; the windows were empty of panes and most of the test tubes and beakers lining the laboratory had been smashed and flung about the room. He had seen a movie recently which showed a room after a hand grenade had exploded in it and it looked just like this place. His hands were wet, and when he glanced down he saw that his arms were covered with blood. All at once, the pain in his back started, pain, though he didn't know it then, that was caused by hundreds of tiny glass slivers that had been driven into his back.

An apparition appeared in the doorway, bloody, wobbling, and Mr. Tao was barely able to recognize his colleague, Mr. Yoshikawa. The two men could only stare at each other, both appalled by what they saw. Finally, Mr. Yoshikawa croaked: "Dugout. We should go to the dugout."

Mr. Tao stood up and the pain washed across his back with an intensity that made him gasp. He staggered, caught the edge of the desk to steady himself, and waited until the waves subsided. He pointed to a steel trapdoor in the basement floor. "There's an emergency steel chamber down there. We will be safe. Let's climb down."

Mr. Yoshikawa nodded, and the two men strained to raise the steel door. But the blast must have knocked it out of line; it was wedged tight, and they could not budge it. The back door was also jammed and the stairway blocked, so they squeezed out one of the small windows and headed for the dugout. There, two other men and one woman crouched in the entrance, peering out at the destruction around them. Mr. Tao groaned, and the woman turned to him and examined his back. Then, slowly, she began to pick the tiny glass splinters out of his flesh.

Suddenly, there was a cry of "Fire! Fire! There are still people inside." Mr. Tao jumped up and ran around to the front of the building. There, a group of people were trying vainly to use an old fire hose, hand-pumping water through it.

They did not know that almost all of the thousands of water mains in the vicinity had already cracked. Mr. Tao shouted for someone to go summon the fire department. But that, too, had been put out of operation.

Over the crackling of flames, he could hear cries coming from inside the building. He grabbed the fire hose and started to climb the wooden ladder that had been propped against the stone front of the building. He pointed the hose toward the second-story window, out of which smoke was pouring, but the pressure generated by the hand-pump was too weak and the water kept falling back into his face until he sputtered and gasped. As soon as he aimed the hose in another direction and the water no longer drenched him, he was conscious of the intense heat. He felt vaguely surprised that a concrete structure could burn so violently. Then he thought of the wooden ceilings and the curtains, desks, chairs and closets in each room. They would certainly burn easily.

Slowly, he climbed down the ladder and backed away from the blaze. He knew it was hopeless now, and when he looked around he saw other buildings burning. Even trees and shrubbery high on the hills were gone, and 50 yards away from him a group of children who had been playing in a circle had fallen where they stood. Some still seemed to be moving. He realized that this couldn't have been just an ordinary bomb. He thought of that new-type bomb he had read about. Maybe this was what had been meant by it.

He stood looking at the building before him, burning so wildly now that he had to move even farther away from it. And then he remembered that steel chamber beneath the basement. If he had been able to get the trapdoor open . . . He trembled in the heat. He would have been baked like a chicken. At that moment, despite his exhaustion and pain, he was very glad to be alive . . .

People deep in dugout shelters were the luckiest. Four-year-old Yoko was sleepy that morning, having been kept awake most of the previous night by an irritated throat. Each time she had tried to relax, the annoying tickle had made her cough and by the time the paroxysm had passed she was wide awake again.

This morning her cough was better, but she found her eyelids heavy, and even playing was tiring. She and her playmates had been building mud fortresses outside a neighbor's house when, at about 8:30, the air-raid siren had gone off. From somewhere, a grown-up had shouted at them to go to the shelter. Inside the dugout, it was dark and still cool from the early morning breeze. Yoko had crawled to a corner and was soon asleep. She never heard the all-clear, nor saw her friends scamper out to resume their fortress-building. Nor did they notice their little friend's absence. At that age, one's universe revolves around a very small area indeed.

Yoko was finally aroused from her nap when the ground under her heaved and jolted her awake. She couldn't see anyone else in the dim dugout, but she heard a deep, continuous rumbling coming from outside, and she crawled slowly out the dugout entrance. There, she sat on the ground, rubbing her eyes, and looked around in terror. All the houses had been knocked down and were burning. Nearby several of her friends were lying on their backs, their eyes staring up at the black sky.

There was a loud explosion from a building a block away, and little Yoko started to cry. Her own private universe had almost disappeared. Whom could she play with now?

In an office near Nagasaki Station, a businessman grumbled as the papers his secretary had handed him spilled to his lap and to the floor. He was just bending behind his desk to pick them up when the room was flooded in light, the east wall blew in and the ceiling collapsed. His secretary uttered one short, piercing shriek and was silent. The businessman, wedged tightly between the well of his solid mahogany desk and the inner wall of the office, crouched in terror in his impromptu little bomb shelter. Three hours later, rescuers had succeeded in digging out most of the trapped victims. The toll at that point had been: 23 injured, 14 dead, including his secretary. He himself was able to walk out of the demolished building with only two small scratches on his left cheek.

Occasionally, the blast had only an indirect effect. At 10:50 that morning, 24-year-old Kazuyo Inao had entered the public bathhouse near the Gokoku Shrine to take her first full-length bath in several weeks. It was her day off from work, and she was looking forward to the unaccustomed luxury of hot water and soap. She had undressed slowly and was about to step down into the sunken tub when a blast hurled her toward it. Her head thudded against the wall and she tumbled into the full tub. Her unconscious body sank slowly to the bottom.

Some twenty-four hours later, reporter Jun Azuma, who had come into the city from the outside, found Kazuyo still in the tub. By then, the water had drained from the many cracks in it. Unlike the blackened, burnt forms he had already discovered, Kazuyo's naked body was unmarked, rosy-red and lifelike. But she also was quite dead.

The blast was especially effective in a city like Nagasaki, and the damage wrought to the flimsy Japanese homes was calamitous. Thatched roofs burst into flames. Wooden walls and rafters fell onto charcoal fires and trapped women and children in burning wreckage. The interior walls consisted of glass or paper *shoji* (sliding screens), so that no inside masonry walls offered extra protection against the blast wind that swept through the Urakami Valley. Many of the wood-framed industrial buildings were of poor construction by American standards, with inadequate bracing and weak joints. Even reinforced concrete structures varied greatly in quality of material. When they were good, they were very good. Some of the concrete buildings near the center of the devastation had been built after the 1923 earthquake and were considered "earthquake-proof." But they were not "atom-bomb proof." Many, gutted and hollow, were at least a foot shorter after the explosion. They had been literally driven down into the earth by the giant fist that smashed down on Nagasaki that morning.

Hard on the heels of the heat and blast came the third killer, radiation, which was probably the most frightening of all because its dangers were poorly understood and it killed silently and invisibly. At the moment of the explosion, various radiation rays were emitted—beta, gamma and alpha rays, X rays and neutrons. The X rays, gamma rays and neutrons injured people. In addition, such fission products as strontium 90 and cesium 137 were scattered everywhere. Called the "Ashes of Death," these fission products held an ever-present threat to those who had survived the heat and blast.

The effects from radiation were felt both immediately and afterward—even long afterward. When the human body receives radiation to the extent of 400 to 500 roentgens, 50 percent of those radiated die, and if the quantity increases to 700 to 800 roentgens, it is fatal to nearly 100 percent of those exposed. Those people within 1,000 yards of ground zero received a more than lethal dose. But, as with heat, the percentage of those who felt the effects of the rays decreased as the distance from the center increased. Wooden buildings afforded minimal protection. Even those inside concrete structures were affected by the massive amounts of gamma rays, neutrons and X-ray beams, especially since some possess the peculiar ability to go around corners.

There is good evidence to suggest that if the effects of heat and blast had been entirely absent from the scene, the number of deaths within 1,000 yards of ground zero would still have been almost as great. The main difference would have been in the length of time it took victims to die. Those killed instantly would instead have lived a day or two, until the radiation destroyed their white blood cells and bone marrow.

Pregnant women had their own unique solution to the bomb—nature, and nature's own special formula, survival of the fittest. All recorded cases of pregnant women within 3,000 yards of ground zero resulted in miscarriages or in premature infants who died shortly after birth. About one-third of the pregnant women beyond 3,000 yards gave birth to apparently normal children; the rest aborted. There is no way of knowing what the effects of that plutonium bomb will be on future generations. But the effects on that particular generation of Nagasaki residents were both immediate and terrible . . .

Isaburo Kubo, the 42-year-old foreman at the Mitsubishi Shipyards and an inspector of electrical parts, was in a small yard within the compound of the torpedo factory. His colleagues here at the arms works had just about completed their work on the new model of the one-man kamikaze submarine, and Mr. Kubo now had to inspect the electrical fittings. He was just climbing into the miniature submarine when a monstrous flash blotted out the sun. Two seconds later, he was slammed into the metal container and both he and the sub were rolled over and over across the yard. Stunned, bruised and bleeding, he emerged minutes later from his metal cocoon. When he saw the ruined factory and the bodies lying on the ground, he realized how lucky he had been. Yet it was a luck that even then was running out. For as he stood there, the invisible radiation was entering his bloodstream, silent radiation from which he would never fully recover.

If an atomic bomb were to burst over your head at eleven o'clock on an average Thursday morning, where would you be in all probability? At work? At home? Shopping? In a machine shop, a beauty parlor, a conference room, an automobile? In just such fashion were the people of Nagasaki caught in the routine of everyday living by the unroutine business of war and a brand-new weapon. Fifteen-year-old Toshiyuki, working as a train crew member, was waiting at Nagasaki Station to board the incoming locomotive and go to work. He was near a huge water barrel when the explosion took place. Flung several yards away, he managed to struggle to his feet. It was then that he smelled something burning. He looked down and was dumbfounded to see that his pants were on fire. Under the circumstances, he did the only thing sensible: He jumped into the water barrel.

Mrs. Yoshiyama was peeling potatoes in her kitchen, and she watched in disbelief as the potato skins flew out the window a second before she was hurled to the floor. Twelve-year-old Moritaka was on his way to school. He had been delayed by the air-raid alarm earlier, and like schoolchildren everywhere, had used it as an excuse to dilly-dally. Blown to the ground by the blast, he did not hear a nearby tree fall beside him. But he did feel the branches and leaves of that tree as they covered him protectively. Mrs. Eto was feeding her baby in a small room in the Shiroyama Primary School, when that building was all but destroyed. Somehow, she and her 6-month-old child lived through those hellish moments. But when Mrs. Eto returned home, she came back to nothing. Her husband, mother, brother, 14-year-old son, 12-year-old daughter, and two other daughters, 5 and 3—all had perished.

Six-year-old Ichinose was playing in the mud with her sisters. She survived; they did not. Mrs. Kosasa was doing housework when the inside of her house turned white and tiles began to fall on her head. She rushed outside and plunged into the small pond in her yard. Then she began to moan as she heard the screams of children who had been swimming in the nearby Urakami River. Of her own three children, one died, one was spared, and one is still living with the very visible scars left by the bomb that day.

Mr. Fujii was on a ferry traveling between Kosuge to Tategami in Nagasaki Harbor. Standing on the starboard, facing ground zero some four miles away, Mr. Fujii's face turned red much like a greatly speeded-up suntan treatment. Eighteen-year-old Taneguchi, who had found a replacement for his own bicycle, was delivering mail. At the moment of impact, the skin was peeled from his right arm, shoulder and back. Subsequently, he spent three years, ten months, in a hospital, but the will to live is strong. He made it.

Mr. Sakaki did not. A 20-year-old streetcar conductor, he was taking his streetcar north toward Urakami when a searing blast turned him and thirty of his passengers into charred corpses. Fifteen-year-old Tomoyo Kishi, a member of the Student Patriotic Corps, was pouring a plaster torpedo mold at the arms factory when she suddenly found herself pinned under the huge plaster mold up to her neck. It took rescue workers almost nine hours to dig her out. By that time, the plaster had hardened and she was incoherent with terror. But she was alive.

There were moments, rare indeed, when the bomb helped someone. At a hospital, two miles away from the bomb center, there was a clap, like thunder, and some of the walls on the south side blew in simultaneously. Mrs. Nishida, trying to complete a painful and overlong childbirth in the delivery room, gasped in terror at the sound of glass shattering. Instinctively, she strained mightily, despite her exhaustion. The baby, a boy, slid easily into the midwife's waiting hands.

But death, that day, was much more common. Little 8-year-old Matsuo was happy that morning. He was playing hide-and-seek with six other boys, around the Chinzei Junior High School on a hillside in the center of the Urakami Valley. Although he had been "it," the one who looks for the others for the last three games, he didn't mind. For this was the first time the slightly older boys had even allowed him to play with them.

Now Matsuo stood in the center of the yard trying to spot the others hiding. When the bomb exploded some 400 yards behind him, he neither heard nor felt anything when the heat rays focused on him and obliterated him. The other boys, huddling in gullies, or crouching behind walls, were completely untouched by those same rays. Minutes later, they crept from their hiding places and walked to where the remains of little Matsuo's body lay on the ground. In horrified silence, they stared at each other. They were the lucky ones, or so they thought.

But once more the invisible killer was at work. Within one year, three of the six boys would be dead from radiation.

CHAPTER 8

The Light of Death

1102 HOURS

FOR MOST PEOPLE THE FIRST PRESENTIMENT OF DISASTER WAS the sudden, intense blue-white light of the explosion. A few people, but a very few, saw Sweeney's plane as it approached the city, or watched it as it circled overhead between the clouds. Private First Class Ikematsu, a former photographer who now served his Divine Emperor as an artilleryman in army unit No. 2739, saw it fly in from the north over the village of Nagayo. That morning, he was 400 feet up on the face of Mt. Inasa, where he was helping with the installation of antisubmarine guns overlooking Nagasaki Harbor. At eleven o'clock he stopped work and headed toward the mess hall where, he had heard, they were all to have a treat for lunch—pork stew with rice and vegetables.

Because Pfc. Ikematsu had once been a member of an antiaircraft unit, he stopped and watched the plane's progress as it buried itself in the high clouds. The day had been relatively clear until the last half hour; now it was hazy and overcast, and the B-29 kept disappearing behind the clouds. He estimated the plane's altitude at about 30,000 feet, unusually high for the B-san. As he stared upward, the plane popped out into an open patch in the sky. It was flying north now, apparently having made a circle of the city. Probably some sort of reconnaissance plane, he thought.

Then he saw a parachute blossom open far up in the sky, and, as it continued to fall, he could make out something dangling from it.* The plane had banked sharply, making almost a 180-degree turn. The next moment the sky exploded, and he closed his eyes against the blinding glare and shielded his face with his arms. But curiosity was too strong and he lowered his arm only to see a silver-white line, rippling in the air, rushing toward him. He heard no sound, but all at once, bewilderingly, he was on his back, and the wall of the mess hall had broken into large pieces and was falling toward him, blotting out the sight of everything . . .

An elderly couple, Mr. and Mrs. Hirayama, must have seen the flash from where they were weeding in their backyard a block away from Urakami Cathedral. Out in the open as they were and less than 600 yards from ground zero, they died instantly, as did two of their three sons at the Mitsubishi Arms Manufacturing Plant. Their eldest son returned to Nagasaki several days later to cremate his family's remains. He was one of the few outsiders who knew what it must have been like for his parents and brothers in those last seconds, for at the time, he had been working at a Mitsubishi plant in another city, a place called Hiroshima . . .

Mr. Kinichiro Hara, the assistant supply chief for the Mitsubishi Arms Manufacturing Plant, saw what he thought

* Actually, it is almost certain that no Japanese saw the free-falling bomb itself. What they undoubtedly saw was the parachuted cannister that was dropped from the instrument plane. The Japanese press was also misled and reported that both the Hiroshima and Nagasaki bombs were dropped by parachute.

was the bomb itself as it fell. He was in the front seat of a repair truck and was on his way to Sage where he hoped to purchase gasoline for the factory. The repairman at the wheel suddenly stopped the truck and grabbed Mr. Hara's arm. "What do you think that is?" he cried, pointing upward out the front window.

Mr. Hara looked up into the cloudy sky and spotted, high above, a tiny parachute with something attached. "That's a bomb for sure!" he shouted and fumbled for the door handle. He managed to get it open, but before he could scramble out of the cab, there came the Light of Death, and both men were flung from the small truck, arms and legs flailing in the hot air.

When Mr. Hara regained consciousness, he found himself face down in a ditch. Waves of pain swept over his back as he rolled over. Lying face up, he stared into the now-black sky, the swirling smoke-mass above him, and all at once he could not breathe. Panic came swiftly and gave him strength to crawl out of the ditch. He gasped for breath, struggling against the great pressure on his chest, then the congestion cleared and breathing became easy again. Off to his left, he caught sight of the repairman, pinned beneath the overturned truck, his head twisted at an unnatural angle.

Despite the pain, he managed to stand up. He had to escape, and blindly, in terror, he began to drag himself away from that spot. Hours later, he reached the Katsuyama School and from there he was taken to the Yami Hospital. For the next three months, he was critically ill, his mind vacillating between dreams and reality. He recovered eventually, but he was a greatly changed man. The bomb had left scars of fear and horror. During those three months, he almost succumbed to the temptation to let the dreams win out. They were infinitely preferable to reality.

Sister Noguchi heard the plane just before she looked up and saw it. She and fourteen other sisters and student sisters of the St. Francis Convent had been working in the field that morning when the plane appeared overhead. Frightened, thirteen of the women had dropped their tools and fled toward the river embankment facing the Urakami district. But 64-year-old Sister Noguchi, who had been in charge of the detail, continued to scatter the fertilizer until it was gone. Then, and only then, did she begin to run from the exposed area, but in the opposite direction from the others. So it was that she came unthinkingly upon an eight-foot-deep gulley. She tried to stop, but her right foot slipped and she began to slide down the rough earth wall.

Halfway down the side of the gully, her fall was halted by a thick oaken branch that protruded from the wall. Ten seconds later, there was a brilliant flash of light, but the terrible heat and blast waves that followed smashed harmlessly over Sister Noguchi's head. When she finally managed to pull herself from the gully, she stared at the barren land, now stripped of all trees and vegetation. Later, she learned that the other sisters had all been killed. Only she, the oldest of the lot, had been kept inviolate . . .

Soundman Suzuki of the Civil Defense Guard had his earphones clamped firmly to his head. Ever since he had received the report that two enemy aircraft had been sighted over Shimabara Peninsula, he had turned up the volume on his headset to the maximum, hoping to pick up the first faint drone of engines from the sound monitor outside his concrete bunker.

At exactly 11:02, Suzuki shot bolt upright out of his chair, his hands pressed against his ears in agony. For a sound had suddenly blasted through the headset, penetrating his ears—a sound that assaulted the senses, vibrating, shattering, numbing—until he collapsed, unconscious, and blood began to trickle from a punctured eardrum . . .

Mr. Kyoshi, the deputy leader of the Nagasaki Water Guard, whose second-floor office window in downtown

Nagasaki faced south, saw only the reflection of a great light on the waters of Nagasaki Harbor. He was utterly astonished. Earlier that morning, he had seen a B-29 circling the city. But no attack had been made, and it was obvious now that nothing had been dropped in the harbor. Then he remembered a message he had received a few hours before from Defense Headquarters: "A bomb, exceedingly destructive in nature, is now being used by the enemy."

Even as he watched, the water in the harbor turned a dull red and the decks of two small wooden fishing boats burst into flames . . .

Mr. Kurokawa saw the plane and considered it just another false alarm. As a telephone repairman assigned to the police department, he had been caught in awkward positions before. It was not all that easy to scramble down from a power or telephone pole, leaving open wires dangling, every time an air-raid alarm sounded. So, when he heard the plane and saw the silver dot floating in from the north, he paid no attention. There had been no alarm, and it wouldn't have mattered to him if there had been.

He was in the process of splicing two wires when the searing flash cut off his eyesight—and his life. There, atop a wooden pole some twenty feet in the air, he roasted like a grotesque human marshmallow, gradually turning black and hanging by the wire line that supported him, as the wooden pole beneath him burned fiercely.

Father Fusayoshi Tamaya probably did not see the blue-white light, screened as he was by the heavy curtain of the confessional box. Although Father Tamaya was only a visiting priest at the Urakami Cathedral, he had spent a busy summer there. Recently, the lines for confession had grown even longer, as the Feast of Assumption Day drew nearer. He knew that his own parishioners back on Kuroshima Island were impatient for his return. Still, it had been pleasant to have this unexpected interlude in Nagasaki, his birthplace and the home of his family.

Father Tamaya came from a large family, with seven brothers and three sisters. For generations, the Tamaya family had lived in Urakami, and his forefathers, his parents, his brothers and sisters, and he—all were Catholics. So it was understandable that after he had graduated from the Yamazato Primary School in 1932, he should enter the Nagasaki Theological School. Catholic parents always had their children baptized and took them to Mass and instruction regularly. At that time, the church fathers observed these children closely, and when they finished elementary school, the priests would approach those who seemed to be cut out for the priesthood and ask: "How would you like to go to theological school?" If the child answered, "I think I might like that," the priests would then visit the parents to get their permission. In young Tamaya's case, it had been Father Matsuda, then priest of the Urakami Cathedral, who had suggested the priesthood.

After completing five years at theological school, Tamaya, then 20, had entered the seminary college at Shakujii, Tokyo. One year after the war started, the new Father Tamaya was assigned to a church in Kuroshima, a small island in Sasebo Bay, about forty miles from Nagasaki. Since priests everywhere were entering military service, some churches, including the Urakami Cathedral, were understaffed. As a result, Father Tamaya had been asked to help Father Nishida at Urakami and had been doing so for the past six weeks.

His presence had been most welcome. An eloquent speaker, compassionate and calm, he particularly loved—and was loved by—children. Often, he could be found surrounded by a group of youngsters laughing and clapping their hands at one of his stories. Even when he had first come from Kuroshima, he had brought a few children along with him and let them stay at his family's house. His one main regret was that he had been turned down for military service because of a valvular disease of the heart. But he had accepted the fact. "It must be God's will," he told his brother Toshiyuki. "Perhaps I am destined for other things." His mother, however, had been openly glad at his rejection. "He does not have the constitution to be a soldier," she had declared. "He is just not strong enough physically for it. It is better that he remain at home, safe and protected."

Earlier in that week in August, Father Tamaya had informed his brother, who at the time was working at the Mitsubishi Shipyards, that he would return to Kuroshima on Friday, August 10. He had planned to leave on Wednesday, but Father Nishida had asked him to stay through the week. He had agreed at once. After all, what difference could a day or two make?

That Thursday at a little after 11:00 A.M., Fathers Nishida and Tamaya were hearing the confessions of the fifty-some Catholics waiting in line in the Urakami Cathedral when the plutonium bomb exploded over their heads a mere 400 yards away. There is no way to determine the exact number present, for there were no survivors. What is known is that over 6,000 Catholics in the Urakami Valley died in that same instant.

It is unlikely that Father Tamaya or any of the others heard anything before annihilation. For in a shattering second, the stately old church and all that it sheltered was no more. The murmuring, the genuflecting, the breathing stopped simultaneously. Only a few decapitated, limbless stone statues of saints in the rear courtyard remained in mute testimony to the bomb's power.

Not far from the Urakami Cathedral, there was a small, frame building which was used for meetings, parties, social events. That summer it was also used occasionally as a ration-distribution center. But on Thursday, the ninth of August, it was being put to use for a wedding, an unusual event at that time in Japan. The groom, however, was on the way to the front. Unusual circumstances often dictated unusual compromises.

By eleven o'clock, the Shinto ceremony had already been conducted inside the hall, and the wedding party had moved from the hot, stuffy building into the courtyard outside. Now people stood chatting in small clusters. Everyone, including the bride, was costumed informally, for a display of formal clothes would have been an insult to others living within the austerity of wartime Japan. Still, their bows to each other were as ceremonious as ever, their manners and dignity unimpaired. Someone in the wedding party had managed to come up with a bottle of sake, and out of small china cups the people toasted the bride and groom. Then the boy and girl toasted each other to the broad smiles of those looking on. They would have just one night together before the boy would have to leave.

No one heard the approaching plane, or if anyone did, he paid no attention. This happy event was to be savored; not one second of it could be lost. There were not many such moments any more.

The group was a short 300 yards from ground zero when the flash blinded them all and turned their bodies into ashes. There were no screams, no moans, only a sharp pop as the sake bottle burst and the rice wine evaporated instantly in the superheated air.

Tsuka Ninimiya, telephone operator for the Nagasaki Telephone Company, was sitting in front of her switchboard in the main office, when a pale light flashed through the window facing her. There was the sound of glass shattering and Tsuka covered her face with her hands. As blood trickled slowly through her fingers from the glass splinters in her face, over 4,000 little lights on the switchboard in front of her simultaneously turned red.

Chief Warden Kiyobei Minami first noticed the blue light as it was reflected off the white paper he was studying. It filled the room all at once, and as he looked up, startled, the wooden wall on the north side of his office began to cave in. The warden immediately crouched behind his desk and watched in disbelief as debris covered the floor. Was it an earthquake? he wondered. Then, as he heard the roaring—like an express freight train outside his window—he knew that it must have been bombs that had exploded very near to him. Somehow his first thought was that the prisoners of Urakami had been right, after all.

Earlier that morning, a roll call had been taken in the Urakami Prison. The 250 prisoners present were asked a pair of questions, the same ones they had heard every morning for the last few months: Did they wish to volunteer to work for the Fatherland Defense Corps and accept whatever job was assigned them? Or did they elect to work in the small factory located within the prison itself? Twenty-five prisoners, those serving life terms and confined to the compound, were not eligible to make their own choice. That morning, of the 225 remaining prisoners, 70 chose to work within the prison itself. The rest were informed that they would make screws for coastal defense boats and plywood torpedo boats, known as "0-4's," under the direction of Mitsubishi engineers.

Warden Minami had been surprised, as he always was, by the large number of men who chose to remain behind. To him, it was a foolish and illogical choice. For one thing, those who volunteered for work through the Fatherland Defense Corps had an excellent chance of having their sentences reduced considerably if they performed their jobs well. Also, there was the honor of doing something important and necessary for the Empire. Surely, even a convict could be patriotic! Furthermore, there was the matter of challenge. Wasn't it more interesting to be engaged in the construction of attack vessels than in the production of uniforms, which was what the small factory inside the prison was involved with?

The 40-year-old warden had tried to figure out the reasons these men might have had for wanting to stay inside the prison. Was it sheer laziness, or bitterness at their plight, or simply resignation, a giving up of hope and response? Was it a reluctance to "volunteer" for anything, or a basic drive for self-preservation? Certainly, some of the prisoners were smart enough to realize that if there were a full-scale bombing raid on Nagasaki, the Mitsubishi Shipyards would be one of the first targets. Perhaps they felt that here up in the Urakami Valley they would be safer.

At about 7:30 A.M., Warden Minami, a dozen guards and 155 prisoners dressed in their green work clothes and peaked caps, had formed ranks and begun the three-mile march to the shipyards. The trip that morning had been accomplished without incident as usual. There had been one instance, a few weeks earlier, of a prisoner escaping. The man had asked permission to leave the workroom to relieve himself and had never returned. That evening, Warden Minami had told the assembled prisoners: "One of your members has abandoned his responsibility and fled on this day. You must all be aware of the grave position that the Japanese Empire finds herself in at this time. Therefore, I warn you not to consider such cowardly behavior. You should work very hard and return to society as soon as possible in order to best serve your country." The warden did not know whether his words impressed the men or or whether they believed that should their fellow convict be caught he would be shot, but there were no more attempted escapes by any of his prisoners.

Shortly after they arrived at the shipyards, the air-raid

siren sounded and the workers and prisoners were sent to the shelters. A half hour later, the alert was lifted and work began. Commander Kamizaki of the Fatherland Defense Corps had stopped by the warden's office, and for quite a while the two men discussed the progress of the work being done by the prisoners. Just before eleven, the commander returned to his own office and the warden returned to his paperwork.

Then, the room had exploded around him. Minutes later, he lurched to his feet and made his way into the hall. There he found two prisoners standing with dazed expressions on their faces. In the background he could hear a voice crying softly, "Mr. Minami. Mr. Minami, I am buried in here. Please, help me. Help me."

Warden Minami recognized that voice and turned to the two prisoners. "We must rescue the commander." But it was not that easy, as they discovered when they pushed their way into his office. For it seemed that the commander was wedged tight beneath a collapsed brick wall. After trying unsuccessfully to remove the bricks from on top of him, one of the prisoners said, "Sir, I have hold of his leg. Shall we try to pull him out?"

Mr. Minami thought for a minute. Other bombs might fall at any time. They could not risk any delay. "Yes, pull him out," he said. "Use whatever force is necessary."

The men took hold of the leg and with two quick, strong tugs freed the trapped man. The commander rolled over. His face was cut and bleeding and his clothes were ripped, but he did not seem seriously hurt.

"Are you in pain, Commander?" the warden asked.

"No," the other gasped. "Just banged up a bit. Better check on the prisoners."

Warden Minami nodded. They were still his responsibility. But it took hours to locate and assemble the prisoners. Several had been seriously injured and had been taken to the aid shelter near the shipyard. At least ten had been killed, but all the guards had been spared. Warden Minami sent one of them to check the condition of the Urakami Prison. Soon after, fires began to break out through the shipyard complex and the men spent the rest of the afternoon trying to keep the fires from spreading. Mr. Minami was constantly in action directing the prisoners in this and other tasks and trying to help the wounded workers and the many outsiders who flocked toward this supposed haven. The guard he had dispatched returned about 5:00 P.M. with a frightening report that he had been unable even to get near the prison. The entire Urakami area, he said, was a sea of flames.

That night, Warden Minami borrowed army trucks to transport the uninjured prisoners to the main prison at Isahaya, twenty-five miles distant. Exhausted, he went to sleep that night in one of the cells, grateful for the hard rest. His brain still whirled with the scope of the disaster, and now that his charges were secure, he could think about his own family—his wife and two children. Chief Warden Takahashi woke him once to say that he had just received a report that Minami's son was safe.

The next morning, he went to the Urakami district. And as he walked, he became aware of a strange phenomenon: the closer he came to what must have been the bomb center, the quieter it became. On the outer edges of the circle of death, there were cries and shouts. As he moved inward, there were moans and soft groaning. Now, as he approached the center of Urakami, there was utter silence.

Then he was standing in front of what had once been the Urakami Prison. The three-building complex had been built on giant concrete slabs. All that remained were those very slabs, cracked and blistered. Everything else had virtually disappeared, for the prison had been a very short 100 yards from ground zero, the closest large structure to that point.

Inside some ninety-five prisoners, fifteen guards and their families, including Warden Minami's wife and small daughter, had perished instantly.

Warden Minami wiped his eyes, overwhelmed at the sight of the concrete graveyard. His own family was gone, but that was not the end of it. In the days to follow, he would have sorrowful confrontations with the relatives of his prisoners and guards.

When the area had cooled sufficiently, he and his men would try to piece together the location of offices, family dwellings and cells, using the foundation of the main building as the only clue. There was not enough left of the bodies to identify individuals. So they had gathered all the ashes together and placed them in one box. When bereaved family members came to claim the remains, Warden Minami would have to tell them: "We are so very sorry that we do not know the identity of everyone. But, please, take home a part of these ashes as a symbol of your loved one."

Mrs. Okamoto heard the sound of the plane from where she was standing on a hillside overlooking the Yamazato Primary School. Ordinarily, she would have looked up to see if she could spot a plane. But this time, she felt a sudden nameless terror, and she jumped down the hill and dove into the shelter. Like a lizard clawing for purchase, she pushed her body against the innermost wall of the shelter. Then, from behind, a blast of intense heat swept over her.

When she finally stumbled out of the shelter, she saw that the sun, which had been shining a few minutes earlier, was now covered by heavy, dark rain clouds. Yet they were like no rain clouds she had ever seen before. These seemed to be moving upward at great speed. In the school playground, she saw that all the women teachers, who had been passing dirt, and the men, who had been digging, were lying on the ground, some silent, some moaning. The upper portions of all their bodies were naked and the hair on their heads and over their eyes had been burned off.

Soon a few young women teachers began returning from the fields with Dean Koga. Their backs were also burned, with red flesh exposed, and the skin hanging down in strips. They complained of chills, and they were shaking badly. Suddenly, Mrs. Okamoto thought of the dark cloth curtains which had been kept in the other shelter. She quickly went and got them and wrapped the teachers in them. Some were already beyond caring.

Mrs. Okamoto heard a voice crying on the nearby hill, and she remembered that she had been standing next to Mr. Sakaki on the hillside. She ran up the hill and found her colleague burned and naked like the others. He seemed to be blind as well and had bitten through his tongue. In his agony, he asked Mrs. Okamoto to kill him. She tried to calm him, but his pain must have been terrible, for he kept pleading, "Kill me, Okamoto-san. Kill me. Quickly!" There was nothing she could do to help him, and the crying began in her heart. He had just completed his schooling in March and had been teaching for only three months. He had been one of the most popular young teachers, particularly with the boys. Now she could only sit and watch as death touched him.

Cradling Mr. Sakaki's head in her lap, she looked out over the Yamazato district and saw that fires had started everywhere. She wondered what had happened to the thousands of children who had lived in that area. At that moment she imagined that she could hear their voices calling their mothers' and fathers' names, those who still lived and who were caught under their crushed homes with the crackling sound of the flames even now approaching them. Her face was expressionless, but the crying in her heart would not stop . . .

Just before 11:00 A.M., Mrs. Okamoto's colleague, Mrs. Adachi, who earlier that morning had heard the forbidden

American broadcast on her radio, had left the digging in the fields and returned to the school building for a cup of green tea.

She took off her sneakers and stretched out her legs. Vaguely, she could hear a radio coming from the barracks in front of the gate. She strained to listen, and was able to make out what the voice was saying . . . "two enemy planes were reported heading over Shimabara Peninsula toward the direction of . . ." Just then she heard the noise of planes overhead. She debated whether she should try to reach the dugout, but before she could move, an intense white light came in through the three windows, making the room so bright that she had to close her eyes. In the next instant she found herself on the floor, nudged there gently but firmly as if by a giant pillow. She watched as the wall collapsed in slow motion. It started to rain—a bruising rain of plaster and wood and tiles.

She must have lost consciousness, for when next she opened her eyes the room was filled with people—or, rather, what was left of people. They must have been out in the field, for most of them had lost some of their clothes—slacks had been ripped and torn away, blouses and shirts stripped off, shoes and sandals snatched away. Mrs. Adachi was horrified at the sight of their exposed skin—arms, legs, faces, breasts, buttocks—all looked like raw red pomegranate. Some moaned and cried, some were silent, others sobbed for "water, please, water." One man, whose skin had peeled away in even red strips, was screaming, "Kill me! Please! The pain. Oh!" One woman teacher, bare from the waist up, was on her knees praying to Buddha. Her voice got slower and weaker and at last she toppled sideways and lay still.

Mrs. Adachi struggled to her feet. She felt ill. She had to get out of that hellish room. Once outside, she made her way slowly through the bodies lying on the ground, trying not to look at their pitiable state. She reached one of the dugout shelters and climbed inside. There she found one of the men teachers who had dived into the dugout when he heard the noise of the plane. Now he stared at her, his eyes wide in shock. "We can't stay here, Mrs. Adachi," he said in a shaking voice. "We must try to help the others." Although all she wanted at that moment was to lie there in safety, she knew he was right. When he climbed out of the dugout, she followed obediently.

In the hours that followed, both teachers filled their water buckets many times from the cracked well, trying in their meager way to bring some comfort to the wounded and dying. It didn't seem to help much. People continued to slip away, one after the other. At one time, she thought of her children, but it was too painful to dwell on that thought. Besides, she was in a strange kind of daze, aware that she moved, yet almost without perception. Once she had been operated on and had received a local anesthetic. She had been conscious of the doctor's actions, yet she had felt nothing. It was like that now.

In the middle of the afternoon, a young policeman stopped by at the school to inquire about his sister, a teacher there. Mrs. Adachi roused herself enough to tell him that she thought his sister had been absent from the school that day. Then, as he was about to go, she grabbed his arm. "Do you know what happened in Shiroyama?" she asked. "Hardly damaged at all," he assured her and left.

An hour later, when she announced that she was going home, she was besieged by requests from other teachers asking her please to find out whether their families were all right. She said she would try, and set out for her own house. Not even her experience at the school, however, had prepared her for the scenes she came upon: streets filled with debris, tiles, broken glass; a yellowish smoke that covered everything and which burned when you inhaled it; corpses of horses, cows, dogs and chickens; the sweet-sour smell of burnt flesh from the charred remains in the streets. In the nearby river, she saw bodies of those people who had come there to drink their last drink floating on their backs and stomachs. And everywhere were people with red faces and glazed eyes, people with limbs blown off, wandering the streets, calling their loved ones' names. Through it all came a continuous wailing.

Approaching Shiroyama district, she was dismayed to discover that the policeman had been wrong—terribly wrong. Shiroyama had been devastated, with almost every building destroyed. Only the concrete Shiroyama Primary School was still standing, and its insides were burning fiercely.

As she moved slowly through the littered streets, she passed a woman who was calling, "Yuki? Yuki? Can you hear me?" Mrs. Adachi thought she recognized her but she couldn't remember her name. The woman was standing in front of a collapsed burning building trying to reach a child who was trapped beneath the wreckage. Every time she would try to get close to the house, the flames would drive her back. "Yuki? Yuki!" she cried. But there was no answer.

Finally, Mrs. Adachi reached what was left of her house—a smoldering pile of rubble. She was able to recognize it only by the twisted well and the crushed water tank beside it. My God, she sobbed. Where are my children? They can't still be in there? She moved forward toward the ashes, but all at once the pain stopped her. She looked down and saw that she had no shoes on; she had walked the entire distance from the school to her house over shattered tile and splintered glass in a state too numb to feel pain. Now her feet were red and swollen and bloody. Abruptly she sat on the ground and stared at the ruins in front of her. It was then that she saw her son's lunch box—smashed and blackened—poking up through the ashes. And she was convinced that her children were dead.

How long she sat there she does not remember, only that

it was almost dark when she struggled to her feet, wincing as the pain from her injured soles swept up her legs. Slowly she began to walk the streets, searching for those beloved young faces, yet not daring to hope any longer. In the distance, she could see the Yamazato school building framed against the skyline. It had started to burn, too.

She came to a dugout on the outskirts of Yamazato and glanced inside. There were people huddling there. And down at the end, their faces turned toward the burning Yamazato school building, were her three children. They must have heard her cry out, for their heads jerked around and they saw her. Then they were all sobbing and hugging and trying to talk at the same time.

"Mother, Mother," her oldest daughter said, "we thought that you had died in that fire."

"And I thought that you had died," she whispered, "but you are not hurt at all."

"We were in the dugout," her second son said. "We forgot our sleeping mats and had to come back here to get them when the bomb went *Bang*."

"Please, Mother," her other daughter pleaded, "don't leave us again."

"I won't," said Mrs. Adachi, trying to hug all three children at once. "I won't ever again."

The great light from the plutonium bomb was probably not intense enough to penetrate the eyes of 12-year-old Kazuyo and register on her brain. And it is not likely that any sound registered. But the heat? Did she feel anything at all a millisecond before extinction? Neither Kazuyo nor her forty-one companions can ever tell us. For at that instant, they were only 200 yards from ground zero, living in a wooden building with a sign which read: Institute for the Blind and Deaf.

Newspaper publisher Takejiro Nishioka saw only the flash from where he was standing on a hillside twenty miles away. But Mr. Nishioka was singularly unlike others who saw the blinding light. For it was the *second* time he had seen such a light in the last three days—and had lived to remember it.

On the morning of August 6, he had been returning from a business trip to Tokyo, and at 8:15 his train had just been pulling into the station at Kaidaichi, a suburb on the outskirts of Hiroshima, when the fission of U-235 took place over that city. After that "lightning flash," he, the engineer and a few soldiers had uncoupled the engine from the rest of the train and started it toward Hiroshima, now almost totally in darkness under the mushrooming black cloud. But they were soon forced to stop because the tracks were jammed with swarms of victims of the blast who were blindly plunging away from the dying city. Mr. Nishioka, along with the other passengers, climbed down from the train. All around on the ground, he could see little flickering jets of flame, tiny bits of burning material like sulfur. Soon his own feet began to get hot and he turned back and joined the fleeing people.

He caught a train late that afternoon from a distant suburb, and a day later he reached his home in Nagasaki. There he discovered that his wife and two daughters had gone to the resort town of Unzen, about fifty miles away, and he remembered that he had urged them to do so. He went at once to the governor's official residence to give him an account of what he had observed at Hiroshima, unbelievable though it was. The governor and his advisors seemed unconvinced of the bomb's destructive capabilities. By then Nishioka considered Nagasaki a very possible future target, as the great port had suffered but five small raids to date, a most unusual circumstance considering Nagasaki's industrial importance and the fact that other cities had been heavily bombed. He urged that steps be taken to protect the city from such a disaster, and the governor agreed that a radio warning should be broadcast to the people.

Early the next day, the eighth, Nishioka and four other editors went to different parts of the city to inspect likely sites for an underground bomb shelter where a newspaper might be published during emergency conditions. After examining several possibilities, they finally settled on a shelter to be built under the hill on which the famous Gokoku Shrine stood, near the Urakami Cathedral. The group arranged to meet on the hill the following morning at eleven to map out plans.

That night, however, Nishioka became quite ill; his temperature shot up and tiny blue spots broke out on his lower legs. He asked that the meeting be postponed, for he had decided to rejoin his family in Unzen. The next morning, he caught the seven o'clock train to Isahaya. There it took him over an hour to locate a cab that would take him to Unzen, but finally one driver agreed.

At eleven o'clock, he and the driver stopped on a hill overlooking Obama, a hot springs resort. While he was chatting with his driver, Nishioka saw his second atomic bomb. He did not know it then, but the Gokoku Shrine where the newsmen were to have met was totally obliterated. Not a stick, not a stone remained of that forty-foot structure.

There is an ancient Japanese legend that tells of a time when from "the floating bridge of Heaven," the divine creators of the world thrust their sacred spears into the ocean beneath and caused to appear the islands we now know as the Japanese archipelago. On that August day, when the sun seemed to burst over Nagasaki, Nishioka had cause to wonder whether those same "divine creators" had decided to reverse the process and transform it into one of total annihilation.

The fact that Nishioka was here, alive, was little short

of miraculous. He had been close enough to the Hiroshima explosion to have suffered aftereffects. After that bomb had been dropped, he had alternately walked and ridden some 400 miles to what he could reasonably expect to be the safety of his own home. Now, sick, confused and longing for his family, he could only stand and watch the churning cloud climb over his beloved city.

Chapter 9

"A Mountain of Rainbows"

1102 HOURS

WHEN A 10,000-POUND BOMB LEAVES A PLANE, THE PLANE actually jumps upward. Seconds after Fat Man dropped out, the bomb-bay doors snapped shut and Sweeney shoved the wheel sideways, taking the plane in as tight a turn as he could. At the same time, he pushed forward, so that they were soon in what amounted to a banking dive. Sweeney's one thought was to get as much distance as possible between them and the bomb.

As the bomb fell clear of the airplane, arming wires were extracted which turned on internal power, making Fat Man completely independent of any signals from the airplane. Separation clocks began running, holding switches open for a certain number of seconds to ensure that under no circumstances could the bomb explode prematurely and blow them out of existence. As the bomb dropped, additional internal switches were closed by barometric pressure at predetermined altitudes. The radar fuses had already been activated and were in the process of sensing the height above the ground by reflection so that detonation would occur at exactly the desired altitude.

But as the seconds ticked off after bomb release, Sweeney was beginning to wonder if they had dropped a dud. "Oh, my God," he said softly to Albury. "Did we goof it up?" He knew that it took fifty-two seconds for the bomb to fall the proper distance, and it must have been at least two minutes already.

At an altitude of 1,500 feet, arming and firing switches closed and the high voltages already built up in the massive condensers in the bomb were released to the many detonators around the sphere of high-explosive charges. As these explosives detonated, they squeezed together the active material and fission occurred.

Just as Sweeney pushed up his goggles in anger, the white light of the explosion came pouring out of the blue sky around him. He squeezed his eyes shut as tight as he could, but the image remained inside his eyelids. When he finally opened his eyes and looked down, he saw the big concentric doughnuts of hot air rushing up at them.

Pappy Dehart sat in the tail of the plane photographing the explosion with a borrowed movie camera. He was also trying to give a verbal commentary of the spectacle, but his astonishment made him almost incoherent. "Repeat, Pappy," Sweeney ordered grimly. "Cannot read. Repeat!" Gradually, it became clear to him that Dehart was trying to describe something that was almost impossible to describe—the visible shock waves racing toward them.

Navigator Jimmy Van Pelt was surprised by the waves when they hit the ship—not so much by the fact as by the number. There had been two distinct shock waves at Hiroshima, but these waves, when they reached the plane, seemed much more intense. When a third wave rocked the ship, he thought that something was wrong. After the fourth wave, he was certain of it. Still one more battered the plane, and Van Pelt thought for a moment that flak had them bracketed. Later, he figured out that the last waves had been a reflection from the mountains which enclosed the valley. To Commander Ashworth, it felt and sounded just like being inside an empty steel trash barrel with somebody pounding the outside with a baseball bat.

Fred Olivi's thoughts were jumbled by the sight. Through the plume of smoke he saw a great mass of flame within a salmon-colored cloud. He had never seen anything like it. Those poor Japs, he thought. But they asked for it!

Jake Beser, pinned to the floor by the sharp turning maneuver and the increase in air speed, was concerned about the plane being stretched to its limits. He guessed that it was problematic whether the outboard wings went supersonic before or after the plane tore apart. Then Sweeney leveled off and as Beser saw the great flash, he relaxed. There it is, he thought. Just like the other one, only a little bigger.

Up front, Don Albury called out to Bombardier Beahan, "Well, Bea, there's a hundred thousand Japs you just killed."

Beahan did not answer. Staring intently out of the nose window, Beahan had just noticed that the mushroom cloud was dangerously close to them.

Just then, Ray Gallagher at the right scanner window, shouted, "My God! It's coming right at us!"

The minute that Captain Fred Bock in the plane behind Sweeney saw the bomb fall out of the belly of that plane, he signaled to his own bombardier, and the instrument capsule, with its letter to Professor Sagane, was released under its parachute. Some fifty-three seconds later, reporter Bill Laurence saw "a giant flash that broke through the dark barrier of our arc-welders' lenses and flooded our cabin with intense light."

Laurence watched the scene in awe. Every now and then he would scribble furiously, trying to record the unforgettable spectacle for posterity. "We watched a giant pillar of purple fire, 10,000 feet high, shoot upward like a meteor coming from the earth instead of from outer space. It was no longer smoke, or dust, or even a cloud of fire. It was a living thing, a new species of being, born right before our incredulous eyes.

"Even as we watched, a giant mushroom came shooting out of the top to 45,000 feet, a mushroom top that was even more alive than the pillar, seething and boiling in a white fury of creamy foam, a thousand geysers rolled into one. It kept struggling in an elemental fury, like a creature in the act of breaking the bonds that held it down.

"When last we saw it, it had changed its shape into a flowerlike form, its giant petals curving downward, creamy white outside, rose-colored inside. The boiling pillar had became a giant mountain of jumbled rainbows. Much living substance had gone into those rainbows."

From the diary of Dr. Shirabe, Professor of Surgery at the Nagasaki Medical School:

WHEN I HEARD THE DRONE OF PLANES, I GOT UP AT ONCE TO GO TO THE SHELTER, SOMEHOW SENSING DANGER. BUT I GOT ONLY AS FAR AS THE DOOR BEFORE A PALE LIGHT SWEPT OVER ME. I THREW MYSELF IN THE CORNER, CLOSED MY EYES AND CROUCHED IN SMALLNESS AS THE BUILDING BEGAN TO COLLAPSE AROUND ME.

EVENTUALLY, THINGS STOPPED FALLING DOWN, AND WHEN I OPENED MY EYES, IT SEEMED TO BE TWILIGHT. EVERYTHING IN THE ROOM—THE TABLE, CHAIRS, THE CABINET, THE BED AND THE SCREEN—HAD BEEN FLUNG ABOUT. AT MY FEET WAS THE CLOCK WHICH HAD BEEN ON MY DESK. I PICKED IT UP. IT HAD STOPPED AT EXACTLY 11:02.

In the center of the district called Shiroyama, within 1,000 yards of ground zero, stood the house of the Fukabori family. At 11:00 A.M., August 9, Mrs. Fukabori was far from that spot, from her children, from death. Clutching a lunch box, a lacquered wooden lunch box, she was on her way to another house, the one her husband had built for their evacuation from Nagasaki. The family planned to make the move on August 10.

How can I ever forget that day, Mrs. Fukabori wondered, long afterward. How could I have known when the housewives in our neighborhood unit came to me the day before that this day everything would be taken from me. We had planned to go to the woods in the country to gather fuel wood. We all had our lunch boxes, and despite the war, we felt as if we were going on a picnic. There was so little to rejoice about nowadays. I collected more wood than usual, and with my basket piled high, I forgot all about my lunch box. On the way home I remembered it, but tomorrow was another day. I could get it then. Did I have a premonition that this little forgetfulness would determine my destiny? Certainly not. Perhaps only God knows why I delayed my return trip.

As soon as I awakened the following morning, I thought of that lunch box, though for what reason I have no idea. But while getting breakfast ready for my family, the thought left my head. I prepared lunch for my husband to take with him to the steel factory, and the rest of the morning was spent washing the children's clothes and doing all the chores every woman must do. By the time I finished, it was already ten o'clock.

That morning, my three children were at home, my daughter ill with a severe infection, and the two boys had a day off from work. When I left to return to the woods, I asked them to care for everything and they agreed at once. It was a holiday for them.

It was a hot, sticky day, and I walked slowly. In the river below, summer-vacationing children were swimming. Some boys were very cautiously removing stones from the river, apparently trying to catch eels. Mirrored on the surface of the river was a big, green camphor tree, its reflection trembling in the ripples. Near the tree, some of the older children were diving from the bank into the deep water there. Leaning against the railing of the bridge, I watched them for a while. They seemed so happy.

There is the house of our acquaintance to the right of the pass into the woods. As I passed by, I called out a greeting, and the woman of the house answered immediately as if she had been expecting me. "Come in and have a cup of tea, Fukabori-san," she called. Though nothing would have been more pleasant, I was determined to get the lunch box first. I told her I would stop on my way back. How could I know that those few minutes would be the dividing line between life and death?

Ten minutes later, as I untied the lunch box from the tree where I had left it, that dreadful light flashed and I was pushed to the ground. As I looked back, I saw a column of smoke rising in the pass I had just come though. In an instant, the smoke spread far and near, and then fires were breaking out all around, even in the woods where I was. It took such a little time.

I did not know what it was but I realized this much: Something terrible had happened. I ran down to the house of my acquaintance, but it had been crushed and was engulfed by flames. I was unable to see anyone there. I began to feel anxious about my own house, but I could not go in that direction. After all, I could not wade through a sea of flames. Almost unconsciously, I went westward through the woods toward the house we had built for us to evacuate to tomorrow. How could we have known that tomorrow would be too late?

On a hill beyond the woods, I looked back toward the Shiroyama district and saw thousands of fires. A great pillar of smoke was rising from the steel factory and I knew then that my husband must be dead. I managed somehow to reach our house in Nishi-town. Fortunately, this house, built midway on the side of the mountain, remained intact. As I looked down, I saw a hell on earth, with Yamazato, Matsuyama and Okamachi all in flames. I thought of the people crushed under their fallen houses, and others jumping around like mad because of the burns they had received.

The afternoon passed in a daze, and that night I could not sleep, but could only think of my family. Had my children been able to escape? Around midnight, the fires began to die down, and I finally fell asleep.

The next morning I went out early. I had to find my family no matter what had happened. I passed through small fires and smoldering lumber. There was nothing around me but a scorched earth; the roads and houses that had had their places under the sun yesterday were no longer to be seen. No one living was in sight in that wide district of Urakami. As I walked deeper into the town, there lay a tremendous number of people burned to death on the street. Their smell stung my nose. Everything there presented a sight which was unthinkable on this earth.

I was out along the streetcar tracks. The rails were twisted as far as I could see. The streetcar that used to run there was now just a metal frame and four wheels, around which lay scores of bodies. By this time, my senses were numb and I was walking near the mountain of Kawanohashi below Matsuyama. In the shallow part of the stream there, I saw the corpses of children as they lay one upon the other, blocking the free flow of the water. I covered my face with my hands. Tears streaked down my cheeks, but I was almost unaware of them. I prayed for the repose of their souls. I had seen only yesterday how happy they looked playing and swimming in this stream. Now they were all gone, never to come back. They were just starting their lives, with many years to live. I felt so sorry for them.

The old, large camphor tree which used to extend its shelter over the river had disappeared. Nowhere could I find simple weeds which I wanted to lay on the bodies in place of flowers.

Unable to stand the sight any longer, I rose and started to walk. I stumbled over the fallen stone walls and broken houses and finally I reached the lot where my house once stood. There was nothing left intact there, not even a piece of wood. Everything had been reduced to ashes. I stood there like a ghost, looking at nothing. Then, burrowing in the rubble, I discovered the white bones of my three children.

All was gone now. The shared confidences, the secret smiles, the touch of loved flesh on loved flesh, the children, those fruits of trust and love—all was no more. It was as though I had perished too, so great was the void within me.

I wished that I had *died* with my children, instead of being alive and alone.

Reporter Junji Sato of the Nagasaki branch of the Domei News Bureau saw the flash and without reasoning flung himself and his bicycle to the side of the road and rolled into a shallow gully running beside it. He tried to push his face into the earth, to merge his body with the ground.

Then, just as the skin of his exposed cheek, fingers, and the backs of his calves began to smart, came the sound. There is a Japanese expression, "a tremendous clash like a hundred claps of thunder behind one's ears," and to reporter Sato the explosion of the atomic bomb bursting over Nagasaki sounded exactly like that. The giant thunderclap was followed by a continuous roar, with the rumbling fading gradually, then a silence, like the silence of death. For a space of a score of heartbeats not a sound more was heard. Everything—motion, action, even time—seemed to have stopped.

One minute passed—another minute, still another—and Sato remained prone by the road, not knowing whether to move or not. He had no idea what would follow, whether this nightmare would end with only one bomb or whether others might even now be falling.

As he lay in the ditch beside the road, he whispered to himself in that silence, "I am still alive. Whatever has happened has spared me. Others surely are dead. I must be alive to be able to think. But for how long?"

Then came unreasoning anger and he cried out soundlessly, "If I am to die, it will not be by the side of this stinking road. At least, back in my office, I can die with dignity among my colleagues."

So he stood up, he touched his head, his chest, his legs in wonderment and looked around. For as far as he could see, the entire city was covered with thick clouds of dust, with a strange purplish cloud spreading widely overhead. The bleeding sun had almost been blotted out by the black smoke geyser shooting up into the sky.

He managed to straighten the bent handles of his bicycle and made his way slowly along the road. The damage had been extensive, he noticed, with most of the houses completely gutted, their doors and windowpanes blown away. Clouds of dust and smoke rising from the debris were so thick that he could now see only about ten yards in front of him. There were also a few bodies lying on the ground, people who minutes before had been alive and part of this world. Now they were shells, no longer even pawns in the game of survival, and again he marveled at his own escape from death.

When he entered the gate in front of his office building, he saw that all the beautiful French windows were completely bare of glass. "Hey, inside!" he shouted. "Is anyone hurt?"

Seconds later, Managing Editor Yamanaka appeared in the doorway, wearing white bandages around his head. "Well, Sato," the big man said with mock seriousness, "I see that you managed to survive?" Sato could only nod. "Come on in then," the managing editor said gruffly. "There's much work to be done."

Slowly Sato followed his superior. He soon discovered that the main damage inside the sturdy structure had resulted from flying glass. The floors and desks were covered with it, but none of the other staff members seemed to be seriously injured, and most were once again hard at work. Two of the girls, with expressionless faces, were silently picking up the larger pieces of broken glass and piling them in a corner. The sight of their fingers, stiff with horror, lifting the fragments of glass as if they were living things would long remain in Sato's memory. Assistant Police Inspector Ishida had been copying the report on Hiroshima when the bomb exploded. Wondering what the great flash of light was, he had quickly leaned toward the window to look out, and the blast wave had hurled jagged glass splinters into his face. At the moment, one of the stenographers was removing them, and painting the wounds with Mercurochrome.

The managing editor had been in his usual place at the time, in a corner near the east window. He, too, had turned at the flash, and one large pane of glass had ripped across his forehead. Despite the blood that immediately gushed from the wound, he had jumped for the phone, realizing at once what had just happened. He had no way of knowing whether the telephone line was still intact, but his actions were automatic. Later, it was found that while all telephone, telegram, electric light and other utility lines within the city had been instantly knocked out, the Domei telephone line between Nagasaki and Fukuoka had somehow remained in operation.

Gripping the phone tightly, Mr. Yamanaka had cried: "Hello, Fukuoka, Fukuoka. Nagasaki has just caught it from the new-type bomb. Can you hear me? I say, the new-type bomb. The entire city has been enveloped in dark clouds. I don't know yet how many have been killed and wounded. We will send you a detailed report as soon as possible."

Now, the managing editor stood by his desk, regarding Sato quizzically. "Sato, do you realize what an opportunity you have?"

"An opportunity?"

"This could be a great story. Can you do it?"

"You mean go out there and—"

"Exactly. Go out there and bring me the facts. What happened? How many dead? Where was the center?"

Sato shook his head. "I don't know . . . My mother . . . my sister . . ."

"Later," the managing editor said impatiently. "You can find out about them later. But now we must report exactly what happened."

Sato's mouth tightened. "All right," he said. "I'll try to find out."

Once outside, however, he did not know where to start. Somehow, his usual cool reasoning had deserted him. All he knew was that the managing editor was right. It would make a great story. He hoped he had the stomach for it.

Where would be the best place to start? he asked himself and nodded at the answer that popped into his head. The next moment he was pedaling for the air-raid shelter of the Defense Headquarters which right now seemed a most reassuring haven. The shelter had three entrances, each equipped with a thick iron door and a shield wall in front. Inside was a huge room with a tunnel which led to the Air Raid Guard headquarters, the office of the Defense Headquarters chief, a room for his staff, a press room, and several other rooms. It was among the best air-raid shelters in the city.

When Sato arrived, the motors of the electric power plant in the shelter were whirring and electric lights were on—the only place he had seen any since that original terrible flash of light. The Defense Headquarters chief, Nagano (the same governor that Sato had seen earlier in the day), his staff, security men and various reporters had already assembled for the previously scheduled press conference which Sato had forgotten all about. As they talked, however, Sato realized that they were blocked from taking any real action by one circumstance: In one stroke, their entire communications network had been cut off. No information was available; no one really knew just what the situation was. The group had thus been reduced to a talking unit which at the moment was trying to determine how to report the dropping of the bomb on Nagasaki to the central government in Tokyo.

In that discussion, Sato was able to make a contribution. He broke in to say to the defense chief, "Domei's telephone line is still open to Fukuoka, so perhaps we could get a message through for you." Governor Nagano, heartened by this unexpected news, instructed his staff to draft an "emergency report" to be sent to the home minister.

Just as he finished, there was a sudden noise outside one of the entrances. It turned out to be the male and female clerks of the prefectural government, pale with fright. They were only the beginning of what proved to be a steady stream of people, often injured, coming down from the hill to the north to seek refuge in the shelter. They entered in a single file, and to Sato many of them looked horrible, as if they had bathed in heavy boiling oil. Their skin was light gray and so badly burned that in some cases it would peel off at the touch of a finger. With their swollen, bloodless faces, they looked like ghosts.

A Korean worker, with a purple, bloated, shirtless body, staggered into the defense shelter. Crumpling in the middle of the passage, he begged, "Give me water, please. I am in great pain." Sato was ashamed of what followed. He could not seem to move, to respond to that plea for help. Moreover, none of the persons nearby, seeing the frightful condition the man was in, went near him. Later Sato found that his condition was typical of many victims who were closely exposed to the blast, but at that moment the body of the Korean, the first dreadfully injured person he had seen, was repellent. Minutes elapsed before Sato mustered the courage to offer the victim water, but by then the man was already dead.

With the appearance of so many victims, Defense Headquarters now realized that the bomb must have caused heavy casualties and they decided to mobilize all the physicians into an emergency aid unit. The trouble was that there was no way of communicating with them. Fortunately, the doctors went to work on their own, trying their best to cope with the aftereffects of this unknown weapon. Because of the lack of communication, however, systematic and coordinated relief activities by the doctors in the city were never put into effect.

About an hour and a half after the explosion, Defense Headquarters got its first report from the center of the devastated region; it came from the Mitsubishi Steelworks. A man of about 30, with a pale face and clad in workman's overalls, ran into the shelter and cried, "Help us, please. Many of my fellow workers have died. There are also great numbers of injured. Can't you send us doctors?" He then began to cry helplessly, but stopped himself and went on with his story. "The steelworks have been totally ruined. The entire region of Urakami is enveloped in flames. The casualties are so numerous that I have no idea how many there are. I alone have struggled over the hill to this place."

Listening to the man's words, Sato was suddenly alarmed.

His sister, Teruko, was working at the munitions factory not far from the steelworks. "What is the condition of the arms factory?" he asked the workman.

"I only know that the region beyond Urakami Station is in raging flames," the man repeated.

Minutes later, when Sato walked out of Defense Headquarters, he heard someone yell, "The prefectural government building is on fire."

He looked in that direction. From where he stood, on top of a slight hill, he could see that an area about 100 yards square, centering around the prefectural building, was burning furiously and sending up thick black smoke. The scene was awesome, a huge daylight conflagration the likes of which Sato had never seen before. He took a deep breath and moved purposefully toward the Urakami area, about a mile away. He had a story to report.

For the next two hours, Sato wandered through the city working his way northward, observing and taking notes. Always, the reporter side of him—objective, analytical—was in conflict with the human, emotional part of his personality. He had to steel himself against the pitiful scenes he came across—a mother, tears pouring down her stricken face, holding a dead mutilated baby and staring at the smoking wreckage of what had once been her house; an old man, almost naked, silently inching his way along the road with sightless eyes and blackened arms outstretched before him; the dozens of children with lost, stunned faces, stumbling through the streets in search of parents, of homes, of refuge; the smell of things burning—wood, cloth, grass and flesh; the physical devastation of man-made structures toppled by man-made weapons. As he neared Urakami, he came upon a "baked" streetcar, which probably had been running at the very moment the bomb exploded. The car was charred, and the passengers, burned to cinders like little mummies, were still sitting in a row at the windowseats on both sides. Sato shuddered and stumbled away.

He noticed that some people seemed to wander aimlessly, but most were obviously searching for someone, some loved family member. Fathers who must have been at work and had been wounded themselves now tried to make their way through the flaming city to where their houses had once stood. Mothers with their babies huddled in shelters wondering if their husbands were still alive. Teen-agers, many of them members of the Student Patriotic Corps, suddenly found themselves cut off from home and family. Hundreds died with the word "mother" still hanging on their blistered lips.

Few families had been together that morning, and so, for the rest of the day and into the night, the city was filled with black, tattered forms who shuffled from group to group, asking if anyone here was from so-and-so section. If someone mumbled "yes," the eyes would fill with hope. "Have you seen my wife, Mrs. Yamamoto, and my young son Sadao?" There would be a slow, dazed shake of the head, and the man would turn and plod away exhaustedly, hoping to find someone, anyone who *knew*.

In some parts of the city, there was only a great quiet, as if all life had departed from that spot. And in that stillness, Sato was conscious of the glass constantly under his feet; it crunched as he walked, and he was amazed at the vast amount of it. Every so often as he walked, he encountered little pockets of sound from which rose steady, wailing cries. At last, his own eyes filled with tears and he closed his notebook and turned in the direction of his own home.

When he rounded the corner into his block, he felt an enormous sense of relief to see that his house apparently was still intact. He walked in and found his mother on her knees cleaning up the glass. "Are you all right, Mother?" he asked. "You are not hurt?"

"I have wiped the tatami mats three times already," his mother said in a sorrowful voice. "But there is so much glass. I don't know where it all came from."

"Where is Teruko?"

"I don't know. I was just going to look for her."

"I don't think you should go out there."

"Yes. The girl down the street who works in the same factory as Teruko returned home with only slight injuries But she said that many other people have been killed and badly hurt. I must go find Teruko."

"At least, wait until tomorrow," he pleaded. "If she doesn't come home tonight, I will go to the bombed area in the morning and search for her. She's probably all right." But he was wrong. Teruko had died sometime within the first ten seconds after the blast.

She nodded, then said: "Do you want something to eat?"

He shook his head.

He left the house then and continued his investigation. When he returned to the office later that afternoon, he found everyone glum. News of the Nagasaki bombing had just been reported by the West Japan Army. The announcement had stated:

> The West Japan Army Command announced at 1415 on August 9 that at about 11:00 A.M. on August 9 two large enemy planes invaded Nagasaki City and used something like the new-type bomb. The details are still under investigation, but damages are believed to be comparatively light.

The people in the office bitterly resented the announcement. They pointed out the windows to the sea of flames as far as the eye could see and the burned bodies in the streets, and demanded: "How can the military call these damages and casualties 'light'?" Sato could only agree with their bitterness. He had seen far more than they had and he knew the extent of the havoc.

There was, however, a valid reason for the announcement. The Nagasaki Fortress Command was located near the mouth of Nagasaki port some four miles from the center of the explosion and behind two hills. Therefore, direct damages sustained by the Fortress Command consisted of but a few broken windowpanes. As the severed communications lines prevented them from knowing the real situation outside of the command post, the commander judged that the damages were small. Since it generated its own electric power, the Fortress Command transmitted its report based on the mild effects they experienced to the West Japan Army, which, in turn, made it official.

That night, Sato wrote his story, his account of his investigations. He tried to keep it factual, to avoid "editorializing," to make it simply a report of the bombing and the damages caused by it. It read in part:

"On the morning of August 9, at approximately eleven o'clock, a new-type very powerful bomb exploded over Nagasaki City resulting in thousands of dead and wounded citizens. When the bomb exploded, the entire region of Urakami, the center of the bombing, was turned into a virtual wasteland. The old city area in the heart of Nagasaki City also sustained fairly heavy damages, and some of the people there suffered burns from the heat rays. The houses in that vicinity were destroyed to the extent they would have been had they been near the center of a conventional bomb explosion of the 500- to 1,000-pound class.

"Within a radius of about 1,000 yards from ground zero, men and animals must have died instantly from the tremendous heat and blast pressure; houses and other structures have been smashed and crushed, and fires broke out everywhere. The strong steel beams of the Mitsubishi Steelworks were bent and twisted like jelly and the roofs of the reinforced concrete buildings were crumpled and smashed in, indicating a force beyond imagination. Trees of all sizes have been torn out by their roots or broken off at the trunk.

"In an area between 1,000 and 2,000 yards of ground zero a great many people and animals died at once, others were injured. Doctors here seem to be puzzled by one effect of the bomb which is causing great discomfort and suffering, and turns the skin first white, then red, then black, though there seem to be no visible indications of severe burns, Fires, as of the night of August 9, were still raging through the northern part of the city.

"Among the government and public offices and buildings found to have been destroyed either by blast or fire are the Nagasaki Municipal Office, the Nagasaki District Court, the Nagasaki Prosecutor's Office, the Court of Appeals Building, the Urakami Prison, the Municipal Water Building. The schools destroyed include the Nagasaki Medical College, the Normal School, Keiho Junior High School and the Chinzei Junior High School, the Commercial School, and the Nishizaka, Zenza, Yamazato, Siroyama and Fuchi Primary Schools.

"The principal target seems to have been the Mitsubishi heavy industry complex. Totally destroyed were the two Mitsubishi arms factories, the Mitsubishi Steelworks, two plants of the Mitsubishi Shipyard and scores of contracting factories in the Urakami area. The Tategami Plant of the shipyard and the Mitsubishi Electric Company also sustained heavy damage.

"At this point, there has been no information released about the nature of the new bomb. Many people have labeled the bomb *'pikadon'* (flash and bang). Some believe that its power is generated by the sun, since both bombs were dropped in daylight.

"The moment the bomb was detonated, power lines, telephone lines and all other communication networks in the city were cut off. The publication of the Nagasaki *Nippo* came to a complete halt as the printing shop fell within the center of the explosion, and the head office was also destroyed. The delivery system for the *Nishinippon Shimbun* was also disrupted, with many of the delivery boys dead or wounded. Thus, for a few days at least there will be no daily newspaper in Nagasaki."

(When the managing editor read the last paragraph, he immediately decided that Domei would put out daily bulletins to inform the citizens of important news. These would be posted on the bulletin board outside the building, and in the days to follow, passersby would gather in small groups to read the news bulletins and peruse the lists of known dead and wounded.)

"Because of the intense and widespread effects of the bomb, all the emergency forces, organized by the military and government authorities, such as rescue work, disposal of dead bodies, first-aid medical care, and general restoration work, have been unable to perform their duties effectively. There has been one notable exception: The emergency food supply plan, which has been able to cope with the hungry people."

(It would take reporter Sato another two weeks to get all of the details of the operation, but when he did, he would sum it all up: "Under this project, which had been organized in advance with great care, boiled rice balls, enough for 4,500 meals, were brought in by trucks from nearby villages on the day of the bombing alone. According to the records, 195,000 meals were supplied on August 10, 114,000 meals each on the 11th and 12th, and 116,000 on the 13th. When the war ended, on the 15th, some 644,350 meals had arrived to feed the people of Nagasaki, morning, noon and night.

"The rice balls came from neighboring towns and villages, even from as far away as Omura, three hours' train ride from

Nagasaki. The people in charge of food distribution worked in twelve-hour shifts. When they were through with the morning round of food distribution, they would find lunches awaiting delivery. It was extremely difficult to keep the food from spoiling in the stifling heat and to distribute it among victims who no longer had a fixed address.")

"One of the most difficult and painful problems in the city has been the disposal of the thousands of dead bodies. For one thing the city crematorium, the only one in Nagasaki, was destroyed by the bomb. Dead-body disposal teams have now been organized by the police aided by the Workers Patriotic Association. But the bodies are still too numerous to be dealt with, and citizens are urged to bring dead relatives and friends to vacant lots for cremation."

Reporter Sato stopped and looked out of the window into the night. Even now red flames were lighting the skies from the impromptu crematorium in the nearby school grounds.

He let his mind drift over the events of the past three days. After twelve hours of continuous investigation and evaluating, it seemed clear to Sato that Japan had suffered a mortal wound in three successive blows: First Hiroshima, then the Soviet entry into the war, finally Nagasaki. If the Americans had more new-type bombs—and it seemed likely that they did—no nation could survive against them. Indeed, it would be folly even to try. He was convinced of that.

That evening, the war minister, General Anami, spoke. He said: "I believe that if we fight through, even if it means eating the grass and sleeping in the fields, we will be able to find a way out. This is the embodiment of the warrior spirit of *Nanko,* of doing everything to save one's country as long as one has life, and of the *Tokimune* spirit of throwing away all human lusts and charging forward to crush the enemy. I call upon all soldiers to devote themselves to defeating the enemy in the very spirit of *Nanko* and *Tokimune."*

Reporter Sato deliberated on the general's words, and concluded that General Anami was wrong. The enemy could never be defeated now. He was sure of it. After hours of shock and indecision, his careful analytical mind had begun to function once more.

CHAPTER 10

The Diamond Workers

THE BOMB EXPLODED SOME THREE MILES FROM THE PRIMARY target which was urban Nagasaki. But if Sweeney and Beahan had tried to drop it where they did, they could not have picked a more effective spot. Had the bomb exploded in the heavily-populated "old city," it undoubtedly would have resulted in a greater number of deaths. But industrial Nagasaki was concentrated up in the Urakami Valley. As it turned out, the bomb went off at a point almost equidistant from the three most important war factories in that area—the two Mitsubishi Arms Manufacturing Plants at Ohashi and Morimachi and the Mitsubishi Steelworks. In one lightning stroke, Nagasaki's war-making potential for heavy armaments was destroyed.

Mitsubishi! In those days in Japan, the very name implied supreme power, a centuries-old family institution that was almost omnipotent. Yet, even today, after the great monopolies have been broken up, it is almost impossible for an American to conceive of the continuing importance to the economy of a company like Mitsubishi. Imagine, if you will, an American combine made up of General Motors, General Electric, U. S. Steel and R. H. Macy's. Such a combine is Mitsubishi. In Japan you may ride in a Mitsubishi elevator, sail on a Mitsubishi ocean liner, buy a Mitsubishi refrigerator or color television set, drive a Mitsubishi auto, cook on a Mitsubishi stove, fly a Mitsubishi airplane, cool off with a Mitsubishi air-conditioner, dress in clothing from Mitsubishi, take medicine made by Mitsubishi, drive a tractor or power lawn mower built and sold by Mitsubishi, live in a Mitsubishi-constructed house, with electric wiring, heating and furniture by Mitsubishi.

In the war years, Mitsubishi was even more powerful, if that can be imagined, and Nagasaki was one of the southern strongholds of the Mitsubishi heavy industries. In that Kyushu city, the Mitsubishi Shipbuilding Company had three separate shipyards adjoining one another. There were two branches of the Mitsubishi Arms Company—the one at Ohashi which manufactured torpedo bombs for airplanes, the other at Morimachi which made oxygen torpedoes for submarines. There was the Mitsubishi Electric Company, the Mitsubishi Power Plant and the main Mitsubishi Steelworks—all within a radius of two and a half miles. More than 40,000 people were employed by Mitsubishi in August of 1945. Many thousands of Mitsubishi employees were killed or seriously wounded when the bomb exploded near their factories.

For 19-year-old Misu, a waitress in the cafeteria of the Mitsubishi Parts Company, it was a time of scattered, barely remembered scenes. There was the recollection of innumerable cups of tea served that morning. There was the moment when she heard the sound of planes, and quickly crawled under a table in the almost deserted cafeteria. Then came the blast, the noise, the room full of thick yellow smoke and a sensation of choking.

Hours, or was it minutes? later, a man lifted her to her feet and told her: "Your back must be badly cut. Your white blouse is all red in back." But she felt no pain, and continued to regard everything through a kind of numbing curtain. At one time, she was lying in a field of potatoes with many other moaning people. As if in a bad dream, she saw a young woman approaching, smiling happily and crooning, carrying a baby in a blanket. She stopped in front of Misu and nodded at the baby, wanting Misu to look. When she peeked inside, she saw a tiny black body without any lower torso. Suddenly, she realized that what she was looking at had shortly before been a living baby, and she was wretchedly sick to her stomach.

Flashes of recall came and went. There was the picture that formed in her mind some time later of a middle-aged man pulling frantically at the debris covering what had once been the cafeteria. Then his face came into focus and she saw that it was her father, and she ran to him, clung to him, as he sobbed: "My little Misu. I worried so much. So much about you."

Finally, there was the memory of the cremation ceremony for her mother six months later. That gentle woman never complained of the growing ache in her body, the loss of weight. At last she slipped away as gently as she had lived. The image was strong in her memory; as if she had been high above looking down at the small group. She saw the young woman who was herself and who had been holding her father's hand and staring first at the tiny urn filled with ashes, then up into the deadly sky.

Two blocks away from the parts company was the five-story-high electric company building. All morning, two carpenters had been working on the roof, constructing a wooden storage bin. At about eleven o'clock they stopped for a break, and as they stood chatting in the center of the roof they heard the sound overhead. They glanced up and saw a single B-29 high above.

"Maybe we should get to the shelter," said one, the taller of the two.

"No. I don't think it's necessary," said his stocky companion, a Mr. Matsumoto. "The Americans never bomb from so high up."

Seconds later, they were almost blinded by a brilliant white light, and, automatically, both men started to run, one toward the exit, the other, Mr. Matsumoto, toward the stone parapet. When the blast reached them, it flung the taller carpenter against the concrete center shaft of the building, and his head made a dull thunk as it smashed against it. He was dead before he fell.

The blast caught Mr. Matsumoto near the parapet, picked him up and flipped him over the edge. He fell 53½ feet (it was later measured) and landed upright, his stubby legs still churning. In through the ground-floor door he ran, his eyes wide, his mouth framing sounds that would not come. He stopped only when he saw the assistant manager gaping at him. Then, when he realized where he was now and where he had been seconds before, his eyes rolled in his head and he crumpled to the floor—out cold!

In the years to come, Mr. Matsumoto would tell his friends of his incredible experience, but they would shake their heads in disbelief. "But it's true," he would wail, and he would explain how experts thought it was the abnormal air pressure that enabled him to float to the ground unscathed.

"Fifty-three and a half feet?" they would scoff. "Mr. Matsumoto, aren't you exaggerating it a bit?"

"But it's true," Mr. Matsumoto would cry. "It really happened."

And it did. Just that way.

Mr. Yamaguchi had a day off, his first in two weeks, from his job at the Mitsubishi Steelworks. That morning he had prepared breakfast for himself and his wife, though he believed that that was a wife's function. Still, Mr. Yamaguchi was worried. She was over eight months' pregnant and the heat and humidity were affecting her greatly. It would be their first child and his wife had never been very strong, but fine-boned and delicate. Now with food so scarce, she looked like a wraith—a wraith with a big belly.

She had slept for the last two hours and he had just given her a cup of tea and was walking back to make his own, when a strange, powerful light came in through the window. Two seconds later the roof fell in, and Mr. Yamaguchi found himself on the floor by the door. He looked toward the mat where his wife had been lying and saw three timbers crisscrossed over that spot. He rushed toward it crying, "Michiko! Michiko! Are you all right?"

There was no answer. Then, as the dust began to settle, he heard her gasping. Now he could see her. She was clutching her stomach, but seemed otherwise unhurt. "Michiko!" he called again.

"Anata, I am all right," she said in a tight voice. "But you had better fetch a doctor. Our child will not wait any longer."

The next hour was a nightmare for Mr. Yamaguchi, as he stumbled through the devastated neighborhood trying to find a doctor, only dimly aware that the city had toppled in ruins about him. He finally found a doctor, but that worthy man looked at him as if he were crazy. "A baby? Fellow, don't you realize what's happened? People are dying. I have no time for babies."

About four blocks from his house, he came to the military barracks and in desperation ran inside the partially burning building crying for help. He was in luck. So it was that twenty minutes later, a 48-year-old army doctor, whose most recent medical experience had consisted of treating venereal disease and gunshot wounds, delivered a five-pound baby to Mrs. Yamaguchi.

Her husband, standing by the shattered window, looking

out onto the desolation, heard the baby's angry cries and rubbed his hands clumsily across his eyes. He gazed outward, toward the fire and smoke, and heard the faint cries of new life. How very strange, he thought, that even in the midst of death, life insists on going on. Out of the ashes a new human being emerges.

Slowly, he walked over to his wife and looked down at her smiling face—and at his new son.

Mr. Torahachi Tagawa had joined the Mitsubishi Arms Factory at the age of 16 and had worked there for the past 24 years. Now, at 40, he was a foreman with 510 workers under his supervision. Starting in 1941, the factory had put out 300 91-type torpedoes a month. But since late in 1943, it had been most difficult to maintain this level, as more and more experienced workers had been called into service and replaced by drafted, unskilled people and students of the Patriotic Corps. At present, over 75 percent of the workers were drafted factory hands.

Shortly before seven that Thursday morning, Mr. Tagawa left his house as usual and walked the short distance to the factory. Before starting work, however, there were the customary warm-up exercises for the employees which Mr. Tagawa led. Afterward, at his command, they all turned toward the northeast and bowed deeply to the Imperial Palace in Tokyo, praying that the divine guidance of their Emperor prevail in their country's struggle. Finally, Mr. Tagawa saluted the factory director, and presented his summation of the day's roll call.

That function had assumed important proportions recently. When Mr. Tagawa had first arrived that morning, the unit chiefs of the factory had given him their roll-call tallies. There were absentees, more than usual, and appropriate action had already been taken. Members of the security section were at present calling at employees' houses to find out the reason for their absence. If they claimed sickness, they were required to show doctors' certificates substantiating the claim. If they were unable to produce a valid reason for not being at work, they were brought forcibly to the factory. Since late 1944, punishment for habitual absentees by whipping had been initiated. Foreman Tagawa had himself taken on that duty on occasion.

When the work whistle sounded, Mr. Tagawa returned to his office to prepare the work projects for the day ahead. He had been given the blueprint for a new "top-secret" weapon —part of a rocket engine—and as he was studying it, his boss, Engineer Koga, entered the room. "Can you get the special part finished by tomorrow?" he asked.

"Yes. I think we can do it by then. May I ask what it is to be a part of?"

Engineer Koga replied, "I cannot tell you now. But soon, perhaps . . ."

Although Mr. Tagawa, an experienced technician, had studied the blueprint of the part, he had no idea what exactly would be made of this component. The naval officer assigned to the factory had said, "When the project is completed, it will make us doubly powerful. You will see." *

A few minutes later, Mr. Tagawa went out into the workshop where Technician Takemura was even then working on the component part. Tagawa watched the young man's absorption, then asked, "When do you think you can get it done?"

"Oh, very soon, sir. But what do you think about that angle?" he asked, pointing to a tiny fusing of thin strips.

* This top-secret project was actually the development of the world's first plane to be equipped with rocket engines. This prototype interceptor, called *Shusui,* or "Autumn Water," would be able to climb to 30,000 feet in three minutes, and thus engage the high-flying B-29s. On the day the test model was ready, Japan surrendered.

"Let me see . . ." The two men worked together, oblivious of all else, until the air-raid siren forced them to stop.

"I must make the rounds," said Mr. Tagawa, straightening. But already most of the workers had gone to the shelters. Half an hour later, the all-clear sounded, and they returned to their tasks.

When Mr. Tagawa went back to his office, he found Engineer Koga puffing a cigarette. "A false alarm, eh?" said the heavy-set scientist.

"Yes. These false alarms don't help us any in meeting our schedule."

"I know. It's a difficult enough job as it is."

For the next two hours the men worked out the details of the week's program. Close to eleven o'clock, nature called Mr. Tagawa out of the office, and as he walked to the privy near the factory he was joined by fellow-foreman Morita. The two men were standing side by side at the wooden urinal when they heard the sound of aircraft.

"Listen! Aren't those planes?" asked Mr. Morita.

"Yes. But they don't sound like ours. They're too high."

"But how can—"

At that instant, a piercing ray of light blinded Mr. Tagawa and he was hurled under the long washstand, where he lay on his stomach with Mr. Morita on top of him. He heard a thunderous roaring and along with it the sound of buildings collapsing. The roof and outer walls of the lavatory fell inward and he could hear Mr. Morita grunting as he suffered the full impact of the falling debris. At last, quietness descended upon them. No longer could he hear the reassuring pounding of operating machinery.

The men crawled slowly out from beneath the washstand.

"Are you all right?" he asked Mr. Morita.

"I think so," replied the other, gingerly feeling his head.

"They certainly hit us this time," he said, and when he

went into the factory building, he saw that they must indeed have suffered a direct hit. The roof had tumbled down, and machines, tools, cabinets and all other equipment had been turned upside down and scattered about. The workers, lying in grotesque positions, were either dead or injured. He rushed to his office only to find Engineer Koga lying dead, face down, about three yards from his, Tagawa's, desk. There was no sign of the clerk and the office girl he had left when he had gone to the lavatory.

Once again, Mr. Tagawa went into the main room. He was sorry he had, for all around him severely injured men and women bleated at him, "Help me! Help me, Mr. Tagawa!" Gritting his teeth, he was able to free a few who had been trapped beneath falling timbers. He told them to get to Kawabira if they could.

Then, through the dust and the smoke came stumbling the figure of the deputy director of the factory, Mr. Fukuda, bleeding from the head and crying, "Is it you, Mr. Tagawa? I am injured."

"Take it easy, sir. I will fix your wound." He hurried back to the office and managed to locate the emergency bag. Mr. Fukuda was squatting, his hands clasped to his head. Mr. Tagawa knelt beside him and gently picked the glass splinters from the side of his head and jaw. Then he painted the whole area with Mercurochrome. "Are you able to return home by yourself, Mr. Fukuda?"

"Yes, I think so. Thank you for your help." He pulled himself upright with difficulty and Mr. Tagawa watched him totter away.

He tried to help several others in the room, but he concluded that medical assistance was required. Once outside the building, he noticed that the oil in the drums just beyond the door had caught fire. With a wind blowing, there was danger that it would spread quickly. Picking up a bucket, he filled it from the water tank beside the drums and tried to put out the flames. It was useless. Then someone shouted, "Foreman Tagawa, run away. It's too dangerous now." He could not see the speaker but he knew that it was good advice. He dropped the bucket and fled.

Until he passed through the factory gate, he had no idea that other parts of Nagasaki had also been hit. Now he was stunned at the sight that unfolded before him. Nothing green was visible on the ground; trees and telephone poles had been uprooted or snapped off. All the houses for as far as he could see had been crushed flat. And as he stared at the enormous devastation, he suddenly began to worry about his wife and 11-year-old daughter. He turned away from the ruined factory and began to run.

A short distance from the factory stood the Iwayabashi Bridge. As he approached it, he saw the bodies of dead and wounded on the street, but he could not stop for them. At the foot of the bridge, he paused, looking eastward. From there he should have been able to see his house. But when he located the block, he saw no houses at all, only burning rubble.

Again, he ran and came finally to his own loss. His house had been torn to pieces. He began to call out loud for his wife and daughter, but there was no response. He stood staring at the ruins, still and dazed. His wife and daughter had seen him off to work only that morning with smiles on their faces. Now what had become of them?

Then he braced himself and realized that he could not simply remain idle. He must search for them, and he turned and headed for his parents' house, a little way down the slope. But it, too, had burned down and no one was there to answer his shouts. Further down the hill, he found his grandfather's house, crushed, too. A short distance away, he saw Mrs. Nishimura, his next-door neighbor, lying in the shade, badly burned. "Do you have any idea what has happened to my wife and child?" he asked her.

She gave him a pitying look and said, "Ah, Mr. Tagawa. Your wife went out just before the air raid saying that she was on her way to the paddy to do some weeding."

Ashamed for a moment that he had done nothing for this poor woman, but beset by concern for his own, he could only murmur, "Thank you. Thank you." Once more, he started running, this time toward the field near the Iwayabashi Bridge.

As he neared the railroad tracks, he spotted Mr. Takasaki, one of his neighbors, talking with a woman who lay at the foot of the railroad embankment. She seemed to be asking him to do something, ". . . come across my husband, Mr. Tagawa, will you tell him where I am?"

The words registered slowly. Then he stopped and gasped. My God! That woman must be his wife. He came closer and stared in horror. Out in the open as she must have been, the front part of her body was bare and burned black, with strips of peeling-off skin hanging limply. Her eyes, in a face that was hard to identify, looked blankly up into the sky, until they swiveled and focused on him. Then she tried to raise herself, whispering, "Oh, dear husband. I'm so glad you've come."

He could not seem to move. "You . . . you're injured," he said at last.

"Could you . . . could you get some water?"

But he had no water with him, nothing to give her, when water was all that she wanted. Suddenly he remembered the brook a short distance away. "I'll get you some right now," he promised. With that he took off his helmet and rushed to the brook. Scooping up a helmetful of water, he hurried back to his wife. He knew that those seriously burned should not be given water, but at that point he realized that his wife had been desperately injured and might not live. What harm could there now be in a little water?

Raising her head, he watched her greedily gulp the water. "Where . . . what happened to our daughter?" he asked, almost afraid of her answer.

His wife looked at him sadly and her eyes were wet. "She died out in the paddy. Her body is still there."

What could he say? Their only child, their beloved Yaeko! They would not watch her grow up, marry, have children of her own.

"My husband, let us go home now."

He nodded and started to lift her. Then he remembered. They had no home to return to, no medicine, no doctor to help her. But he guessed that a train would be at Nishimachi to take the injured to the hospitals at Isahaya and Omura. "Since our house has been destroyed," he explained, "I'll take you to the train. A good cure for burns is available at Omura." When she nodded her consent, he lifted her and began the half-mile journey to the train stop.

He had been right. When they reached Nishimachi a train was already being loaded with injured people, and he carefully placed his wife on the platform in the rear of one of the cars. But when he tried to climb aboard, a conductor stopped him. "You can't get on. This is a special train for the injured."

His wife apparently had not heard. For, turning to him, her face contorted with pain, she whispered, "You must hurry and get on before the train leaves."

Mr. Tagawa pleaded with the conductor. "My wife is so badly hurt that she can't take care of herself. She needs me." Without waiting for an answer, he started again to climb aboard. But the conductor pushed him down, crying, "You're not hurt. If you get on, some injured person will be left behind. We'll take good care of your wife."

Minutes later, as the train began to move, his wife reached out her hand toward him, crying, "Why don't you get on? Quickly! The train is leaving."

He began to run alongside the moving train. "You'll be all right," he shouted. "Go to the Omura Naval Hospital. I'll see you tomorrow."

Her hand clutched at him. "No. Don't leave me."

"You'll be all right."

As the train gathered speed, he was left behind, and he stopped running. He stood immobile, watching the wooden train get smaller and smaller in the distance. He knew he would never see his wife again.

Mr. Yoshiro Fukuda, the 50-year-old deputy director of the Mitsubishi Arms Factory at Ohashi, looked very much the way most foreigners pictured Japanese men in those days. With his slick hair-comb, his roundish face, his thick, horn-rimmed glasses and his ready, toothy grin, he could conceivably have landed a part as a "typical" Japanese in an American war film then being made.

That morning, he was both frustrated and angry. He had called a conference in his office with six of his key personnel to discuss two thorny problems plaguing the factory's operation: lack of fuel and lack of transportation. Foreman Ichikawa of the forging department, a huge and powerful man, had just told him that they would not be able to keep the plant on full production that night because the supply of coal had been exhausted.

"But the supply chief assured me that a shipment would be arriving yesterday afternoon for sure," he said.

"It never arrived," the foreman said simply.

Engineer Kurata broke in. "You know, sir, that five of our seven trucks are out of commission? Maybe transportation could not be provided."

"Five trucks?" Mr. Fukuda exploded. "I thought it was only two!"

"Three more in the last week," the engineer answered resignedly. "I'm not surprised. They're already being operated on adhesive tape and glue."

"I know, and even that is in short supply," he answered with the old cliché. He turned to the chief of the technical section. "What do you know about it?"

"The supply chief told me that the coal would be arriving, too," answered that elderly gentleman. "By the way, why isn't he here?"

"We'll soon find out," Mr. Fukuda said angrily and picked up the phone.

Supply Chief Shibata was apologetic, but firm. It was not his fault, he insisted. The coal warehouse chief had informed him that they had no trucks available to deliver the coal. Perhaps in two or three days . . .

Mr. Fukuda banged down the phone, turned and started to say something to Engineer Kurata. The words were never uttered. Almost simultaneously, a great light flashed, the large glass window in back of Mr. Fukuda shattered into a million pieces, and the room spun upside down.

Twenty-five miles away in Omura, Mr. Fukuda's wife was astonished when two small windows in the living room suddenly fell in. She had not heard planes, nor an explosion. She ran outside and looked toward Nagasaki. Over that city, she saw a huge cloud mushrooming into the sky, exploding inwardly with what seemed to be red, purple and green flares. She sank to her knees. "Oh, how beautiful," she murmured. "How very beautiful."

Mr. Fukuda regained consciousness slowly, not knowing for a few seconds where he was. His feet were slightly above his head, resting on an overturned chair, and there seemed to be a great weight on his chest. When he opened his eyes wide, he saw that it was a corner of a filing cabinet. He managed to push it off and climb slowly to his feet. His head hurt, but he was alive, and under the circumstances he was grateful for that. For he was certain that they had sustained a direct hit. And he was not at all surprised that this factory had been singled out. He had known for a long time that the Americans would eventually get even with them, with the people here in this factory, even with him personally. After all, it was right here, under his direction, that the torpedo bombs had been produced that were used in the attack on Pearl Harbor. The Americans could never let that go unpunished.

The room was almost completely demolished, with plaster and fallen timbers everywhere. Suddenly, in a corner of the room, he spied two bodies, half buried beneath debris. He clawed his way there, climbing over smashed furniture. It was Engineer Kurata and Foreman Ichikawa, the latter's massive body now merely a broken hulk.

All at once he felt weak and dizzy and was conscious of pain; he felt a burning sensation on his right cheek and arm, and his head ached abominably. He looked back and saw the trail of blood he had left, its bright red imprint stark against the white plaster dust. His head must have been badly gashed. The door had been torn from its hinges, and he stumbled through it to what had once been a hallway. But the walls were gone and he was now in the main room. He moved forward and suddenly Foreman Tagawa was in front of him, steadying him. The other disappeared for a moment, then he was there, applying ointment to his head.

Now, unaccountably, he found himself outside. There, it was a place of torment with people lying on the ground, or staggering in circles, or crawling toward the gates. He looked toward the medical clinic, with an idea of going there, but there was no clinic in sight. In fact, there was no single building that still remained whole.

A fire had started in the wooden mess hall, and Mr. Fukuda shouted for someone to get fire extinguishers. A large number of workers were moving out the main gate, but not one of them paid the slightest attention to his words. Despite, or perhaps because of, their indifference, he felt more than ever that it was his responsibility to do something, at least to find out the extent of the damage. He started walking unsteadily toward the main building and the technical section, but paused when he heard cries coming from people pinned beneath the fallen buildings. He had lost his glasses at the moment of the explosion and could only dimly make out the figures. He stopped a group of five or six men and ordered them to try and rescue the trapped victims. They nodded mutely and set to work. He reached the technical section, but found that it was already on fire. By now, his wounds hurt severely. He knew that he really couldn't do anything at this point, so he joined the exodus out the gate.

Several hundred yards outside, he stopped and looked back. The entire factory was in shambles and burning in many places now. All around him were jostling bunches of people, charred, bloodstained, with ragged scorched clothing, yelling or crying.

He thought of going to the University Hospital for treatment, but dismissed the idea. The hospital had undoubtedly been destroyed, too. Where could he go for help? He had been residing at the home of an aged doctor, just west of the railroad tracks in the middle of the woods. Thinking that he might be able to receive treatment there, he crossed the railroad tracks in back of the factory, noting that they were twisted and uprooted, and walked through a field toward his lodging. But in the distance he saw that the woods were no longer there, only splintered remains of trees, which were already beginning to smolder. All of a sudden, he felt the last remaining strength leave his body and he sank down helplessly in the middle of the field.

He felt very alone, but gradually he became conscious that people were constantly passing by on the nearby road, heading toward the mountains and what they believed might be a safe place. Some of them, recognizing him, called out words of encouragement, and a few of the more venturesome and less seriously wounded actually approached him. They commiserated with him on his terrible appearance and said they were sure that he would be all right. From their tone of voice, however, he knew they didn't believe it for an instant, that they really thought that he was already at death's door. Two sub-chiefs from the factory noticed him lying there and walked quickly over to ask how he was feeling and whether they could do anything for him. He said "no" and asked them if they knew what had happened to the director of the factory. They told him that the director was in good condition. For Mr. Fukuda that was one bit of good news at least. The director was a close personal friend. Mr. Fukuda would not find out until much later that the director died two days after the bomb.

The heat was merciless as he lay there in the scorched field, and he drifted in and out of consciousness. It must have been hours later that a subdepartment head, Kubo, came to him in that sweltering place. Mr. Fukuda, gasping and barely conscious, asked him for a drink of water. But, unbelievably, the younger man refused his superior, saying that if Mr. Fukuda drank water, he would soon die, and would Mr. Fukuda "please try to understand." He could not give him any water. Instead, Mr. Kubo, using the very shirt he wore, set to work erecting a makeshift sunshade over the deputy director. And when Mr. Fukuda complained that the hard ground made his wounded head unbearably painful, Mr. Kubo managed to find a soft pillow somewhere. Mr. Fukuda would always remember how soothing that pillow was and how grateful he was for Mr. Kubo's kindness.

From that time on, Mr. Kubo remained by his side, while Mr. Fukuda alternately writhed under the searing sun and felt violently sick to his stomach. On three separate occasions he felt as if he were breathing his last and pleaded with Mr. Kubo to take him back to the plant where he wished to die. But Mr. Kubo once again refused, telling him that the entire plant was on fire now and that he was much better off lying here and resting. Soon, he could be moved.

After a while, Mr. Kubo and another man half-carried him to the remains of Michinoo Station. There he was helped aboard an emergency train along with other badly wounded. Mr. Kubo shook his hand, and Mr. Fukuda was surprised to see tears in the other man's eyes, as he told him that he had to remain in the city, but that Technician Iwasaki would accompany him as far as Omura Hospital.

He had been set down in the middle of the aisle where the traffic was heaviest. So Technician Iwasaki stood over him, protecting him with his own body, all the way to Omura. In one week's time, this same guardian would be dead of radiation burns.

Also one week later, Mr. Fukuda's white blood cell count would plummet to 800 from a norm of 5,000 and doctors would give up all hope for him. Then, miraculously, he would recover completely, with only a few minor aftereffects. There would be no logical reason for his recovery, when so many others similarly afflicted would perish. Nor for the fact that of the seven men in his office that morning, he, and he alone, survived.

As far as he personally was concerned the bomb turned out to have a strangely healing power. For some ten years before the bomb fell, he had been suffering from a painful stomach ulcer. Later, doctors would tell him that the rays of the bomb entering his office window that morning had possibly acted like a giant X-ray machine. He hadn't understood it all, but he knew that from that time on, he had no further problems with his stomach. One good thing, at least, could be said about the bomb: It had cured Mr. Fukuda's ulcer.

CHAPTER 11

Two Fliers

1115 HOURS

CHUCK SWEENEY, KICKING HIMSELF OVER THE FINAL TWELVE-minute delay, took *Bock's Car* south, away from Nagasaki and toward Okinawa, with *The Great Artiste* right on his tail. With the extremely critical fuel situation, he knew that he should have left the target area immediately after the drop. But Beahan had to have a firsthand look in order to write his strike report of the damage. Besides, he himself had an overpowering urge to see exactly how effective the bomb had been. He had made one complete circle over the doomed city, trying to evaluate the effects, but the heavy smoke obscured everything. Now he wondered whether those extra minutes had consumed vital fuel.

"Pilot to flight engineer," he called on the intercom. "Kuharek, how about giving me a rundown on the remaining fuel?"

"Roger. It'll take a few minutes to calculate."

By that time the mushroom cloud had risen to a height of

some 60,000 feet, and Ed Buckley, watching it from his scanner's window, turned to Radioman Abe Spitzer. "How do you feel now, Abe?" he asked.

"Would you mind shutting the hell up?" Spitzer growled.

"I feel the same way," said Buckley, "only a little bit worse."

When Sweeney had first seen the mushroom cloud, he had been gripped by a sudden feeling of disaster. What have we done? he wondered, and just as quickly he answered himself. What we have done is our job, he told himself. We are soldiers in the service of our country, and we are here to win a war that we didn't start. But we're damned well going to finish it!

Chuck Sweeney had been picked by Colonel Paul Tibbets to fly Special Mission No. 16 for one simple reason: Tibbets believed that Sweeney could get the job done. All his life, Sweeney had "got the job done." Good-natured, extroverted, likable, Chuck Sweeney was still a born competitor, a fighter, a finisher of things once started. He had seldom failed in anything he had attempted.

Born in Quincy, Massachusetts, just outside of Boston, Chuck Sweeney was the second oldest boy of six children, five boys and a girl. His father was a plumbing and heating contractor and close to all his children. He was particularly fond of Chuck. He admired the boy's drive and imagination. At the age of 10, Chuck had had a newspaper route. By 14, he had organized the other boys in his neighborhood into a reliable "newspaper delivery company." He collected one-fourth of a cent per paper from each of the other boys. He no longer had to deliver papers personally. But, as "boss," he was expected to protect his boys from outside encroachment and to settle internal differences. He did both extremely well. Although he looked chubby and soft, his ample flesh covered well-developed muscles. Chuck Sweeney was both strong and tough, as Irish-Catholic boys in the Boston area have always had to be to succeed.

In high school he was an average student, popular with his classmates—boys and girls—and he was on the football team. In his senior year, the halfback on the team was an All-State selection. Chuck Sweeney had been his blocker. At six feet one inch and 190 rock-hard pounds, Sweeney was even then the one who "got things done."

He worked with his father for a while after graduation and then entered the leather business. But he had already made up his mind what he was going to do: He wanted to fly. He joined the U. S. Army Air Force Cadet program in April, 1941, eight months before Pearl Harbor. "I'm the kind of guy who always thought he ought to have his own plane," he recalled. "Then the Government comes along and offers to teach me to fly one, so I figured I might as well get in on the ground floor."

Sweeney soon found he had made the right decision, for he was a "natural" pilot, with that rare combination of flying instinct and quick learning ability. Moreover, he loved to fly. "The one bad thing flying did for me," he told Albury once, "is that it soured me on automobiles. I don't believe in them anymore. Too damned slow. Why ride when you can fly?"

By 1943, he was a 23-year-old captain at Eglin Base in Florida and had flown just about every kind of plane used by the Army Air Force. He was desperately anxious to get into action but now his flying ability worked against him. He was just too good to be taken off his job as test pilot. Then Paul Tibbets came to Eglin with the prototype of a new bomber, the B-29, and Sweeney fell in love with the big plane. "Colonel Tibbets came in at dusk, flying that great big beautiful machine," he had told Beahan. "My God! My tongue was just hanging out to get into it. I had dinner with the colonel the next evening and asked him if there was any chance of getting transferred to his outfit." There was, and a year later Sweeney and Tibbets were at remote Wendover Field in Utah.

Before Wendover, however, he had drawn an assignment as a test pilot for B-29s at Grand Island, Nebraska. For Sweeney, his most memorable "pupil" was Curtis LeMay, General, USAAF. One morning Sweeney was waiting beside the test plane for his first session with the famed LeMay when, cigar clamped between his teeth, that stocky individual strode briskly up to him.

"Captain Sweeney?"

"Yes, sir," said Sweeney, saluting. "Ready to start flying, sir?"

LeMay stared at him. "I never fly an unknown quantity, Captain. Dismiss your crew and come with me."

The two men proceeded to a nearby hangar where a B-29 was undergoing repairs. LeMay ignored the men working on the ship, and simply climbed inside. Sweeney followed, reluctantly, and the two men sat down in the pilot's and copilot's seats.

"Now, Captain," LeMay said blandly, "you are supposed to be an expert on the B-29. Well, make me an expert."

"Sir?" Sweeney was nonplussed.

"Start talking, Captain. Talk to me about the B-29, about construction, props, rpms, stabilizers, ailerons. Tell me what you know about this plane. Tell me *everything* you know."

Pinned by those ice-blue eyes and the most penetrating questions he had ever had to answer, Sweeney talked. He talked about the B-29 as he had never thought he could. "I didn't realize I knew as much about the B-29 as I found I did that day," he recalls.

At the end of six straight hours without food or drink, Sweeney was exhausted, his uniform wet with perspiration. Curtis LeMay had finished his fifth cigar and his eyes were even bluer than they had been earlier.

At last he rose and, shifting his sixth cigar in his mouth, he looked long at Sweeney and nodded, apparently satisfied. "Thank you, Captain Sweeney. Now let's get some lunch."

"Yes, sir!" said Sweeney gratefully and followed the general out of the plane and out of the hangar. Sweeney was certain that General Curtis LeMay knew exactly as much about the B-29 as he did. That incredible man had picked his mind as clean as a repossessed house, as they say in Massachusetts.

A month later, Sweeney was snatched away from Grand Island, and sent to Wendover Field, or "Leftover Field," as Bob Hope once called it. There Sweeney became an integral part of a new "hush-hush" operation, code-named Centerboard. There had been the endless practice bomb-drops, then Tinian, Hiroshima, and finally Nagasaki.

Now "Centerboard" was almost over, and Sweeney's mouth tightened over the memory of what had just happened. It was ironic in a way. All his life Sweeney had been afraid of just one thing: guns! Now they had just dropped the biggest "gun" in history.

"Skipper," Kuharek's voice broke into his thoughts, "we have about three hundred gallons left."

"Roger." He pushed the intercom button. "Pilot to radio. Abe, I think Major Beahan has finished the strike report. Better get it out as soon as possible. Then alert Air-Sea Rescue. Tell them we're heading for Okinawa."

"Roger." A few minutes later Spitzer was tapping out the strike message to Tinian: "Bombed Nagasaki 090158Z visually with no fighter opposition and no flak. Visible effects about equal to Hiroshima. Trouble in airplane following delivery requires us to proceed to Okinawa. Fuel only to get to Okinawa."

Spitzer was completely unsuccessful in reaching Air-Sea Rescue. His messages to them were simply not answered. He had no way of knowing that Air-Sea Rescue, having heard nothing about the delay over Kagashima or the aborted run over Kokura, had assumed that the mission had gone off without a hitch and that Sweeney's plane was even now nearing Tinian on its return trip. They had packed up their Dumbos and Superdumbos and gone home, never suspecting that *Bock's Car* was over three hours behind schedule and was probably going to need them.

Kuharek, watching the fuel gauges, suddenly realized that they were still eating up too much fuel. Now he suggested to Sweeney, "Skipper, we better cut down on our speed, way down."

"Roger," said Sweeney at once, and the plane slowed.

Sweeney thought it was a good thing that they had left the scene when they had. The boiling purplish-white cloud had assumed threat proportions for him at the exact moment when he remembered a certain paragraph in his orders: "Under no circumstances will your aircraft fly in or near the smoke from the explosion. It will undoubtedly be radioactive and highly dangerous."

Sweeney wondered for a few seconds whether they had flown too near as it was. Then he put those fears from his mind. Fuel was a much more immediate problem. He hadn't told the others, but he was pretty sure they were going to have to ditch.

One person who would have been most interested in that part of Major Sweeney's orders about not flying near the cloud was Second Lieutenant Nobukazu Komatsu, a member of the Sasebo Navy Cadet Corps. For when Sweeney was streaking away from the mushroom cloud, Komatsu and his two crew members were in a Japanese seaplane heading right for it. Komatsu did not know exactly what they would find in Nagasaki, but he had made a guess, for he remembered a conversation among his fellow pilots only yesterday afternoon.

The discussion had been about the type of bomb the Americans had dropped on Hiroshima. A communiqué just issued from 901st Air Corps Headquarters had stated: "Hiroshima has been damaged to a considerable extent by a new-type bomb." Cadet Komatsu and his fellow pilots knew that this brief announcement had to be an understatement. For on the evening of August 7, one of the cadet corps planes had been flying over Hiroshima, and the pilot's personal reports of the devastation had been almost too fantastic to be believed. He had stated that the entire city had been destroyed and that fires were still raging everywhere. He could only guess what must have happened to the people down there. And all that havoc had been caused by just one bomb.

The Americans themselves had confirmed the happening. It was just before dinner that Cadet Komatsu and several other cadet pilots had heard President Truman's proclamation on a shortwave broadcast from the United States: "A bomb with the explosive power of more than 20,000 tons of TNT has just been dropped on Hiroshima, an important army base," he had declared. "It is an atomic bomb. It is the harnessing of the basic powers of the universe. The force from which the sun draws its power has now been loosed against those who brought war to the Far East."

The cadets had argued over the American President's words. What had he meant? What the devil was an atomic bomb? Exactly how had the "powers of the universe been harnessed"?

"It has to be something like a giant torpedo exploded in the air," said one cadet.

"No. It's much more powerful than any torpedo."

"Maybe it's powdered magnesium," ventured another. "That would account for the great flash that was reported."

"I think it has to be a combination of many elements."

"Still, I can't believe that it was an explosion in the air. How was it set off? It must have exploded on the ground."

"I heard that it was dropped by a parachute, so maybe it was set off by some sort of timing device."

As they had talked, Cadet Komatsu realized that they were all groping in the dark. Not one of them had the slightest idea of what an "atomic" bomb was. It was an entirely new concept not only to the cadets but, he was certain, to most of the military as well, else he would surely at least have heard the word "atomic" before this time. If it was indeed a new type of bomb, he felt it was his duty as a flyer to learn all he could about it. He could not fight the enemy effectively without knowledge of all his weapons and how they performed.

He already had an advantage over most of the other cadets in that he was reasonably battle-seasoned. Just eight months earlier, while flying cover-protection for the Sekigama ferry steamer, his plane had been attacked by an American Grumman fighter. All the others in his plane had been killed. Though he had been wounded and was consequently exempt from further military service, he had seen the great need for Japanese fighter pilots, and although technically his cadet corps was a training unit, it had already assumed the function of a fighter squadron. He had rejoined his group without hesitation.

Other young men all over the Empire were doing the same thing—for Japan's need in August of 1945 was desperate. The air force was not alone in its manpower predicament. Every arm of the military felt the pinch, and not only in a shortage of men but also in an almost complete lack of supplies, fuel, equipment, weapons and ammunition. The air force had only a pitifully small number of planes still flying and hardly any bombs and ammunition. That was one of the main reasons for the Kamikaze plan. With limited planes and bombs, these suicidal missions seemed the most effective and economical way to utilize the weapons on hand.

Centuries ago, when the Mongol invader, invincible up to that point, had set sail in a fleet of ships to conquer Japan, the Emperor had prayed for a divine wind to repel the enemy.

Miraculously, that divine wind, the Kamikaze, had materialized in the form of a great typhoon and had totally destroyed the invading force. Now, the order was to create another divine wind, another miracle, in the form of an invincible arm of the divine Japanese Empire. It was hoped that this noble, self-sacrificing force would wipe out the latest foreign intruder.

Cadet-pilot Komatsu had thought a great deal about the new divine wind, these suicide missions. He was a vigorous 20-year-old, and he had certain qualms about how he would face up to the test. He eased his mind with the reasoning that every man is afraid of death, and that he was no exception. Yet he found it easier to plunge into action than to ask others to do the same thing. It took courage to send one of his men to possible death. The phrase "suicide attack" had a certain ring to it, but he found himself waiting for someone to "volunteer" for those missions rather than choosing someone himself.

The conversation last night had produced no consensus of opinion. Finally, since he was the highest ranking and most experienced pilot present, the others turned respectfully to him. "What do you think, Lieutenant Komatsu?" one asked him. "You have not given your opinion yet. What kind of bomb do you think it is?"

Cadet-pilot Komatsu hesitated. "I do not know," he said slowly. "But I would certainly like to get some firsthand information about this so-called atomic bomb."

Now, he suspected that he was about to get his wish. Actually, the news of a "great bombing in Nagasaki City" had been flashed through cadet corps headquarters in Sasebo at 11:05 just a few minutes before. His first thought at hearing the words "great bombing" was of that "new-type bomb" that had been dropped on Hiroshima. His next thought was that if this indeed was the same kind of bomb, now was the best chance they would ever have to study its nature. He didn't think he need wait for any direct orders from his commander. The responsibility would automatically fall to his squadron, as it was the closest to Nagasaki.

Since he had the highest rank present, he knew that he could simply give the command, "You go," to one of his subordinates. But he couldn't do it. It was too much to ask of them. He himself would have to take the risk. So he said, "Follow me, those of you who want to," snatched his helmet and hurried out to his seaplane.

As he ran, he wondered if any of his men were following him. When he glanced over his shoulder he saw his good friend, Second Lieutenant Tomimura with a grin on his face. "You are in such a hurry to meet this big new bomb, my friend?" He chuckled. Komatsu never appreciated his friend's sense of humor more than at that moment. It lifted his spirits, and when he looked at the other man who had joined them, Chief Petty Officer Umeda, he saw that it had cheered him as well.

The three men took off from Sasebo Base and headed toward Nagasaki, some forty miles distant. The summer sun shone on them between the clouds but Komatsu was unable to see very far ahead. The time was 11:10. It had taken them only five minutes to get airborne.

As their plane neared Nagasaki and they broke through the cloud cover, they found their way blocked by an enormous black pillar of smoke spreading over the sky. Lieutenant Komatsu had never seen anything like it. More than anything else, it resembled a huge volcanic eruption with many layers of smoke rising from it. The black cloud ring was churning like a thing alive, spiraling and twisting in the air as it stretched higher and higher.

Already it must have been close to five miles high, and hanging over it, like the head of a monster, was a gigantic, ever-expanding ball of smoke. He checked his altimeter and saw that his plane was flying at 10,000 feet. The gauge had to be working, but he still could not believe that smoke from a bomb could reach that altitude.

The sun coming from behind gave the illusion that the cloud was undergoing instantaneous changes of colors—from red to blue to yellow—but when they got closer, Lieutenant Komatsu saw that it was only gray and black. From their present height, they could not see the extent of damage in Nagasaki. Komatsu tried circling the cloud ring, but was unable to make out anything down below.

"We can't see anything from here," he shouted. "Let's cut into the cloud." But neither Lieutenant Tomimura sitting beside him, nor Chief Umeda, in the rear of the plane, answered him. Perhaps they were too awestruck.

As they approached the cloud, it became unusually hot inside the cabin. Was the heat coming from the outside? he wondered. With his left hand on the control stick, he opened the cabin window and stretched his hand out. Quickly, he pulled it back in. Even with a glove on, it was as if he had plunged his hand into live steam. He pulled the window shut and saw some sticky dust on his black glove. He stared out the front window, but could barely see through it. On the outside of the glass, huge drops of water had formed which, added to the dust, obscured his view. What does it mean to find bomb dust at this altitude? he wondered. Is the heat due to the fire down in the city? If so, what extraordinary energy the bomb must have had. All Nagasaki surely has been destroyed. And he was about to fly into that ominous cloud. Cold perspiration began to run down his back.

"I can't stand it!" someone shouted suddenly, and when Lieutenant Komatsu turned he saw Chief Petty Officer Umeda vomiting. He must have been directly in the path of the "steam" that had come in through the window. Instinctively, Komatsu tightened his hold on the control stick and the plane streaked into the great cloud.

In an instant, they were in total darkness and he could

see nothing. Normally, even in thick clouds some light from the sun filters through. Here, it was as if someone had suddenly pulled shades down over the plane windows. The temperature in the cabin rose quickly and, dressed as he was in full uniform, he was soon drenched in sweat. Several minutes later, his copilot, Lieutenant Tomimura, who could bear the heat no longer, opened the window. He screamed as the strange odor and intense heat blew in on his face. Lieutenant Komatsu could keep neither his eyes nor his mouth open, and he realized that this cloud was not normal smoke.

"Close . . . the . . . window," he gasped. "Close it! Quickly!"

Suddenly it brightened and he was momentarily blinded by the sunlight. They had passed through the cloud. It had taken them a full eight minutes. Out in the light again, Lieutenant Komatsu noticed gray, brown and black dust sticking all over his clothes, as if he had been following behind a car on a dusty road. Also, either the fumes or the heat had given him a terrible headache and he felt nauseous. He shook his head to clear it and saw that his copilot was busy vomiting.

Lieutenant Komatsu circled over the city, trying to decide what to do next. He opened the window again, and this time there were no fumes or heat. When he stuck his finger outside, however, it was immediately covered with dew.

Since the main purpose of their flight had been to ascertain the damage to the city, he took the plane lower and lower, flying in circles, but he was still unable to see the city through the smoke. Finally, at about 1,000 feet, he saw the city of Nagasaki, blanketed in red flames with black smoke billowing up as if from a crude-oil fire. He tried to go down even lower to take pictures, but the heat became too severe and some of the flames were shooting up as high as the plane.

"We will land in the harbor," he said and instructed his

copilot to inform the base of their plans. Tomimura nodded. He had stopped vomiting at last and although he appeared pale and shaken he seemed otherwise all right. Komatsu flew just above the water surface and when he saw there were no obstacles, glided down until the floats slapped against the water of Nagasaki Harbor.

The minute he turned off the engine, Tomimura took off his boots and dove into the water. He had meant to swim to the shore and direct the plane from land. However, the sea was so shallow that he was able to stand up, with the water only to his waist, grinning foolishly. Lieutenant Komatsu smiled back. It was the last time the two men would smile that day.

From where they floated in the harbor, Lieutenant Komatsu was surprised at the relative lack of heavy damage, at least in the main part of town. Quite a few structures had sustained some damage, and a number of fires had broken out and begun to spread, but to him it looked like the aftereffects of conventional heavy bombing, and not of a "super" bomb. Across the harbor, the Mitsubishi Shipyards did not look as severely damaged as they had after the August 1st raid. And the eastern Nakashima Valley seemed almost untouched.

When he looked up the parallel Urakami Valley and saw the giant black funnel of smoke come to earth at its core, Lieutenant Komatsu realized that there was the center of the explosion. About two miles up that valley must have been ground zero. That was where he would find out how bad it had been.

Chief Petty Officer Umeda was still too sick to move from the plane, so the other two pulled the seaplane to the deserted shore and tied it to a damaged pier. They began to walk up the Urakami Valley and, very quickly, it began to get worse, much worse: Buildings smashed flat, telephone poles and trees fallen or tilted away from the blast center. Here the fire had grown rapidly, swooping along with its self-generated wind, so that they were forced to make frequent detours. The heat was intense, and the smoke and the blowing ashes almost suffocating. Soon their faces were black, their eyes red-rimmed.

The people also began to change—much for the worse. Downtown, their injuries had seemed largely superficial. Now, people in various degrees of injury were streaming past Komatsu, some with their mouths open in silent screams.

About a mile from the harbor, they saw a woman partly buried under a crushed house, calling for help. Above her ear was a large open gash from which blood was flowing. Lieutenant Komatsu reached down and pulled her out. She was crying something about her mother and child still being inside the ruins, but, looking at the house, he knew that there was no hope for anyone still inside. There was a sudden searing pain in his leg, and he saw that one of his trouser legs had caught fire. He beat at the flames with his arms and put them out.

Eyes glazed at the sights around them, the two men moved up the valley, and the scenes became more and more heart-rending. They came across people who were naked and hairless. The skin of their bodies was gray and mottled from the burns.

Others, their skin hanging in strips, staggered blindly past them, screaming in agony whenever they brushed against anything. One man's eyeball was hanging out of its socket, and he ran with his hand cupped to his face, babbling incoherently; another kept his mouth open in a perpetual silent scream simply because his jaw had been broken and he could not close his mouth. One couple, tottering along, dragged their skin behind them like animals who were in the process of shedding their outer covering.

On one street they came upon some twenty or thirty people of undefinable sex, writhing in agony. These poor people must have heard the two men approaching because as they came nearer each black mass on the street tried to lift itself, feverishly stretching out hands. They did not speak, but Lieutenant Komatsu knew that they all wanted just one thing: water. He felt sick because he had none to give them.

Then he saw a child of about five years tottering toward them. All his hair had been burned off, and his naked body was swollen with black-red burns. In a faint voice the child said, "Water, please." Moved with pity, filled with compassion, the lieutenant took his hand and gently drew him closer. But the skin of the child's hand seemed to slip off and yellow fluid splattered from it.

Lieutenant Tomimura had located some muddy water, and Komatsu held the child up so that his friend could pour some of it into his mouth. The child drank it, then his head flopped down in Komatsu's arms. The little eyes, sightless beneath the absent lashes, seemed to stare recriminatingly at Komatsu. He saw that his good friend had sat down on the ground and begun to cry like a child himself. Lieutenant Komatsu put the lifeless form gently on the ground.

Silently, the two men resumed their walk. After many detours, they reached what seemed to be the central bomb site. Everything was flat and burned; charred corpses lay here and there; iron pillars were scattered around like melted candy. To Komatsu, there was something very strange about this spot. If it had been the center of the explosion, why wasn't there a bomb creater? He looked for some sign of it, but there was nothing, only a barren expanse. It was difficult to imagine that houses had stood there only minutes ago.

Near the once beautiful Urakami Cathedral, which was now just a pile of bricks and burning insides, they came to what seemed to be a grade-school courtyard. There, in relatively orderly rows, were the dead bodies of children who must have been doing calisthenics when the bomb was dropped. Half a block away, they saw the body of a badly-burned woman lying by a tree. The blackened branch of a young azalea covered her face. Lieutenant Komatsu reached down to brush it off. Then he recoiled in horror as he realized that the thin branch, which could easily have been snapped between two fingers, was riveted in her forehead, thrust there at the instant of the explosion. He stood trembling in silence.

Two hours had passed since they had landed and they had had enough. Without a word, the two men turned and started back the way they had come. This time there was a difference. On their way to the bomb site, they had been too numbed by the first shock of discovery to notice that strange shadows had been imprinted here and there, shadows made by the fiery rays of the explosion. There was, for example, the railing of a bridge which was clearly visible on the pavement. There was a diagonal stripe across the street, probably a telephone pole. They saw the shadow of a man with a megaphone clearly outlined on the ground—he undoubtedly had been standing in an observation post. The shadow was so clear that Lieutenant Komatsu looked around to find the owner of it. But, of course, there was no one.

They reached the shore and found that it was no longer deserted. Dozens of bodies floated in the water, or sprawled near it. These were people who had come to seek water in their agony and had found death instead. The two men had to push dead bodies out of the way of the floats in order to take off. Lieutenant Komatsu was filled with a deep depression. The gigantic cloud was still there after three hours. It had grown even bigger and seemed to be laughing at its victims down below.

Flying back to the Sasebo Base, he knew that he still faced a difficult task. The officers at headquarters would want a complete report of the damage and casualties at Nagasaki. What was he going to tell them? How could he possibly describe what he had just seen? He felt himself begin to tremble again. What he wanted at that moment was simply to blot it out of his mind. But he could not. He knew he would not sleep that night.

CHAPTER 12

"Take Care of My Son"

1130 HOURS

MR. SAKAO KAWANO, A MEDICAL STUDENT FROM NAGASAKI Medical College, was running. Like others in Nagasaki at that moment, his one great desire was to get away—anywhere—and so he ran, blindly, unreasoningly, gasping with the effort and the horror that he refused to look at as he passed.

That morning at the medical school, there had been a special clinical lecture for the seniors by a visiting professor. At eleven sharp, the professor had arrived at the examination chamber, and the lecture and demonstration had commenced. The students had clustered around the professor, with Mr. Kawano just behind him. The surgeon had started to cut into the cadaver when a great blinding flash and powerful blast struck the medical building. Mr. Kawano was blown off his feet, as were the others, but he quickly picked himself up and raced out of the building. He just made it; behind him, he heard the crash as the roof fell in. He stood still and looked back; several of the medical buildings and the hospital adjoining were already on fire. The wooden building where he had just been was crushed flat and flames were spewing from the wreckage.

He sank down on the ground, almost paralyzed with fear. He sat there for several minutes, then scrambled to his feet and, without thought, began to run away from the awful scene, dodging bodies and debris. He reached what had been a main street and it was even worse. He ran faster until he saw a baby boy, naked and crying in front of a wrecked house, lift its arms toward him. As he started toward the child he heard a woman call weakly from under the wreckage. "Please take care of the child. Take care of . . . my son." He could see one bare leg, twisted and burned, sticking out from under the fallen timber. He started nearer but the heat from the fire drove him back. Picking up the child, Mr. Kawano cried out desperately: "Don't worry. I'll take care of your son." There was no answer from the ruins.

Jogging along with the child in his arms, Mr. Kawano felt strange indeed. Whether he wanted it or not, the boy was now his responsibility and he was suddenly determined to protect him with all his might. He had been spared. It was up to him to care for the offspring of someone who had been less fortunate. As far as he was concerned, the boy was now his son.

Where should he take him? He thought of the Nagasaki First Branch Hospital near Mt. Motohara. The baby could be cared for by the hospital personnel. But he would remain with the child. It was the least he could do. The child was quiet, unmoving in his arms, so he began his trek to the mountain, grateful that he was no longer alone on this terrible day.

Passing by the burning Urakami Cathedral, he started to cross the river behind it, and stopped, shocked to his depths. He had seen corpses along the way, but they had only dimly registered. This was a scene he would never forget. Scores of people floated in the river or sprawled on the banks in grotesque positions. About six feet from where he stood, a mother and just-born infant, still linked by the umbilical cord, lay in agonized death. One life had ended even before it began. He clutched his own baby boy even tighter and fled. At last he came to the hospital of Dr. Sakurai, the Gentle Doctor.

Dr. Sakurai took the squalling infant tenderly from the young man's arms. Several of the women in-patients were in good condition and he thought that they might want to help.

"I think some of our ladies here can satisfy the boy's more pressing needs," he said, smiling at the young man. One of the women giggled, took the baby and calmly began nursing him.

The infant's loud cries stopped at once and Mr. Kawano sighed deeply and grinned. ' My son," he said proudly.

"Where did you come from?" asked Dr. Sakurai.

"The medical school."

"What happened there?"

"Completely destroyed. I was lucky to get out alive." Then the scene around him registered—the burning hospital, the wounded people lying on the ground. "So it hit here, too," he said.

"I think it hit everywhere," Dr. Sakurai said softly.

For him it had been utterly unexpected. When he had heard the faint whir of plane engines, he had paid no attention to the sound, engrossed as he was in his treatment of a patient. A minute later, a sudden white light bathed the room. Dr. Sakurai whirled to Nurse Ozaki standing beside him, and started to say something. He didn't have time, for at that instant a violent blow struck him on the right side. Swept off his feet, he found himself lying on the floor between two cots, with debris raining down upon him.

A voice cried, "We have been hit. The hospital has been

hit!" and he was astonished to realize that the voice was his own. But the only response was the groaning and crying of the others. Half-blinded by the thick white plaster dust, he managed to stand up. Now he could see that the ceiling and one wall of the room had crumbled and toppled in. The whole area was filled with yellowish smoke and flying white dust. It was dark, terrifyingly dark, for the middle of the day, as if the sun had suddenly lost its brightness.

Then the smoke began to clear a little, and he saw Nurse Ozaki rising feebly from the floor beside him. Though covered with white fragments, she, too, seemed uninjured. But what about the patients? He looked around and saw that most of the cots had been overturned, rudely spilling the patients to the floor. Dimly, he could make out a few forms struggling to their feet. Some were bleeding from heads and faces, their eyes wide with fear. Others were limping toward the doorway with their hands clutching wounds. A few, trapped beneath timber or furniture, did not move at all. What an awful mistake to bomb a hospital, he thought, never imagining that the hospital had not been the main target. But he felt no anger, only a great sadness.

Nurse Ozaki, standing by his side, was looking at him, and he knew that she expected him to do something. Somehow he couldn't move. He felt strangely apathetic. He knew he should act immediately. There were wounded people here, and surely there were even more upstairs. Here on the ground floor they were probably lucky. He could only imagine what had happened to those unfortunate ones who had been on the second and third floors. That area surely had been blown away and all the patients there killed.

"Help, Doctor! Help! Help!" Were those voices coming from the stairs toward the second floor? Yes, and they roused him from his stupor. Now he could see people staggering down the stairs and into the main ward. But they were moving with great difficulty, and when he looked toward the doorway he could see the stairs were partially blocked with fallen timbers. The patients were crawling over them and under them toward the doctor, each crying, "I'm injured, Doctor. Please, help me."

"What has happened up there?" he shouted. "How bad is it?"

But nobody seemed to know what had happened. Dr. Sakurai thought of several possibilities—a ten-ton bomb, or an explosive-laden enemy bomber that had crash-dived onto the hospital?

Miraculously, the patients and staff coming down the stairs seemed only slightly injured, despite the fact that many of them were bleeding and in obvious pain. But their relatively minor injuries made it clear that the hospital had not received a direct hit.

"Is anyone still trapped upstairs?" he asked one of the patients.

"Mr. Harada has been buried," someone cried. "Please go and help him."

Dr. Sakurai started toward the stairway, then stopped as he realized that there was work to do right here. "Everyone out to the yard," he ordered. "Quickly now."

But was it safe outside? He ran out and past the injured patients already in the yard. Near the wall, there was a slight rise and he climbed it and stood looking toward the southwest. His throat became choked at the sight of what had happened to his city. The sky was black and all the buildings as far as he could see were burning.

He heard Nurse Ozaki calling, and he quickly retraced his steps. Her face was worried when he reached her in the yard. "Doctor, smoke is coming from above the third floor."

When he looked up toward the canted roof of the hospital, he saw that it had split in several places and caved in. Now smoke was coming from one of the damaged gables. It might eventually be serious, but right now, compared with the conflagrations that were engulfing the surrounding buildings, it was not.

One of the patients lying on the ground cried, "Mr. Kawaguchi and Mr. Harada are still in their rooms. They could not move. Won't you help them, Doctor?"

"The doctor is doing all that he can," said Nurse Ozaki impatiently. But Dr. Sakurai said gently, "The patient is right. If that fire spreads . . ." He turned and called to Brother Mizuiwa, as big and broad as ever but with his hair now singed. The two men ran in through the front door and carefully climbed the partly-blocked stairs, until they reached the third floor. There they found that the damage had been considerably greater than below, with walls and ceilings collapsed and furniture flung about. He and the monk began to carry out injured people.

Half an hour later, they were sweating and filthy—but they were not finished. For there were still two people pinned under the heavy wreckage who could not be extricated. Dr. Sakurai knew that something had to be done about them—and quickly, for the fire was beginning to spread rapidly. There had been at least two weeks of hot, rainless weather, and the hospital must have been tinder-box dry. The building was some 1,800 yards from the center of the explosion, and its wooden parts had first blackened, then blistered, then popped out in tiny spots of fire which leaped from one dry area to another. Now, it was a matter of minutes. But how to get the two patients out?

It was a bespectacled, 20-year-old seminary student, Takeo Noguchi, who solved the problem by the simple expedient of bringing a saw. Brother Mizuiwa quickly cut through the fallen pillars and beams. The two patients, not seriously injured but very frightened, looked at their rescuers with gratitude as they were cut loose. Strangely, it was Dr. Sakurai who felt the most grateful—that he had been able to remove all his patients, his personal charges, to safety.

Outside, Nurse Ozaki lifted his spirits even further with her lovely smile. "You have done it," she said with a sigh. "There is no one left in the hospital to die in the fire. They have all been rescued, thanks to you."

"Thanks to all of us," he said gently, aware now how great had been her own contribution, how constantly she had been by his side when he needed her. They looked at each other, then quickly turned away. For each had seen something in the other's eyes that had not been there before, and there was no time for that now.

Moments later, his high spirits were shattered when Noguchi ran up to him and said: "Dr. Miyazaki has been very badly hurt. I think she is dying."

He was so disturbed by the news that the strength suddenly went out of his legs, and he had to reach out a hand to Nurse Ozaki's shoulder to steady himself. "Where is she now?" he asked at last.

"Brother Mizuiwa has just gone to the mountain behind the hospital, carrying her on his back."

"Why did he take her there?"

"She asked to be carried to the coolness and the water and the shade," Noguchi told him.

He would have gone to his colleague at once, but just then a group of people came into sight, trudging up the hill toward the hospital from the city down below. As they drew nearer, he could see their ragged condition and hear their moans and cries. Then, another man, big and naked from the waist up, approached from the other direction, holding his head between his hands.

"Doctor Sakurai, I've been injured," the big man said in a trembling voice, clutching at the doctor.

Dr. Sakurai peered at the other man and was stunned to

recognize Mr. Tsujimoto who was a financial backer of the hospital. "What happened to you, Mr. Tsujimoto?" he asked, barely able to support the big man in his arms.

"On the pumpkin farm out there . . . I was picking pumpkins for the patients. Then . . . I don't know what hit me."

It was clear that Mr. Tsujimoto was in bad shape. His head and face looked bloodless. His hair was curled and singed and his eyes were red and bleary with both eyebrows burned off. There were three small, pale, round marks on his red chest, and Dr. Sakurai guessed that they had been made by the buttons of the black shirt, which he habitually wore, when it was burned off his very back. Dr. Sakurai tried to comfort him, telling him to try and find a shady place to lie down and rest. The other man nodded, pulled himself erect and stumbled away, and the doctor was appalled at the change in this once sturdy and powerful man.

Then had come the medical student with his "son." Dr. Sakurai had been heartened at how quickly the young man had gone to work, moving among the patients, trying to reassure them.

A short time later, a middle-aged man staggered into the yard and fell to the ground. He sat there, holding his head in his hands and mumbling almost to himself. "Water. I want water. So hot."

Dr. Sakurai knelt beside him. "What happened in the city? What kind of bomb was it? How were you injured?"

But the man only stared at him with blank eyes. "I'm hot, so very hot," he gasped. "Water, please, water." Then, all of a sudden, he collapsed and rolled over. Dr. Sakurai saw that he had lost control of his bodily functions. What kind of terrible weapon is this, he wondered, to reduce healthy people to incontinent babies?

People just like that man climbed slowly up the hill toward the hospital in increasing numbers during the first two hours after the explosion. They looked just the same and sounded just the same. People, half or wholly naked, moaned, "I'm injured, hot. Give me water." They spoke in hoarse whispers, and their faces were blank, expressionless. At one point Dr. Sakurai imagined that he was dreaming of a slow procession of the dead who were all garbed in white, a sight similar to that which he had often seen in his boyhood days at funerals.

For the Gentle Doctor it was a time of helplessness and frustration. He did not know what was wrong with most of these people, and he had no medicine to treat those with discernible burns and wounds. He and Nurse Ozaki had made a trip inside those parts of the hospital not ablaze to try and find medicine and bandages, but to no avail. The entire four-wing building was in chaos. The precious medicine—liquid and powder—littered the floor of the equipment room. What had not been blown down—a few desks and dressers—stood incongruously upright in the disarray, with drawers halfway open and completely empty.

Neither he nor Nurse Ozaki was able to figure out where the contents of the drawers had gone. Later, he reasoned that the terrific pressure of the blast, passing through the rooms and corridors, must have uprooted everything before it, sucking up even small objects.

Various objects turned up in the most extraordinary places: The ecclesiastic palliums, usually tucked away by the altar in the chapel, were found torn to pieces in the field outside; the books in the library were found all over the hospital, as far away as the basement; pieces of the familiar nurses' uniforms, snatched from dresser drawers, were seen floating in the wind in the yard. Pinned rolls of bandages had been furiously unraveled and torn. Even in the doctor's own room, everything was in disarray. In the closet, all his clothes had been ripped off the hooks and hurled outward. There had been two pairs of shoes, one brand-new, on the floor of the closet. He discovered that one pair had disappeared; the brand-new pair was still there, except that the shiny new laces had been stripped cleanly from the shoes.

Out in the yard, Dr. Sakurai was approached by Brother Mizuiwa. "Doctor, did you know that Father Kawamoto has been injured?"

"How bad is it?"

"I don't know. Maybe you better examine him."

"How is Dr. Miyazaki?"

Brother Mizuiwa thought for a moment. "Her head was badly cut; the chief nurse bandaged it. But I think she has been badly hurt."

"I will go to her as soon as I can. But first, let's have a look at Father Kawamoto."

Father Kawamoto still didn't know exactly what had knocked him out. All that morning he had been listening to Catholics making their confessions. It was eleven o'clock before he found a chance to return to his room to get a book he wanted. He was hurrying back to the chapel and was just passing the narrow part of the corridor at the end of the first floor when there was a flash of light that pierced the dark hallway, and, seconds later, a clap of thunder. The good father was spun head-over-heels through the air. His head smacked against one of the concrete pillars on the side of the hallway and he was momentarily stunned. He had once loved to box and the sensation was exactly like being knocked out by a well-timed blow to the chin.

At last he recovered enough to get up and go on to the chapel, but he found it demolished. He could not understand what had happened; there was no human being in sight. As he reeled from the ruined chapel, Brother Mizuiwa saw him and led him outside.

Now, scrutinizing the priest, Dr. Sakurai was surprised at how quickly his eyes had become swollen and purple. Fortunately, there didn't appear to be any bleeding from his head. He was undoubtedly suffering from concussion, however, and Dr. Sakurai advised him to lie down.

The hospital was now belching black smoke. In the hours it had taken to remove all the patients, the fire had grown so extensive that it now enveloped most of the building.

"Oh, Doctor. Look! The X-ray equipment is burning," cried Nurse Ozaki, standing beside him.

It was true; smoke was streaming out of the basement, a thick, black smoke that could only come from oil. Dr. Sakurai had imagined that the fire would not spread through the concrete floor to the basement, but he had forgotten one thing. A large square opening had been carved through the center of the building from the basement all the way up to the third floor to make room for a new elevator now under construction. Through that space, all kinds of burning objects had fallen, igniting level after level until they had reached the basement. Near the elevator shaft were the three sets of modern X-ray equipment delivered just the day before. They represented half of all the X-ray machines in Nagasaki and had been brought to this hospital for safekeeping. The transformers of the machines were filled with insulating oil. Obviously, that had overheated, exploded and caught fire.

"There's nothing we can do about it, Miss Ozaki," Dr. Sakurai said sadly.

To Dr. Sakurai a great deal of time seemed to have passed since the bomb went off. "Is it near dusk now?" he asked Nurse Ozaki.

"No, it's only two in the afternoon."

He must have lost all sense of time. And probably he was not the only one. For most people, the day must have seemed endless. To him, it seemed that many days had been compressed into those hours since the bomb. One reason possibly was that so many people, seriously injured, had passed before his eyes in so short a period.

In the afternoon, there was a change in the appearance of those who came up the hill to the hospital. Their skin was no longer white and ghostlike; it had turned black and begun to peel off. Most such victims simply collapsed upon reaching the hospital compound. Many others were victims of blast damage, people whose bodies were filled with glass splinters, those who had been crushed by falling houses or who had been hurled against hard or jagged surfaces. All of these terror-stricken people, he soon discovered, had one thing in common: They all seemed to think, "*I* was the only one who was hit by the bomb. *I* am in pain. Won't you help *me* first?" It really didn't make any difference in the order of his "treatment." For there was little he could offer besides comfort.

At one point, Nurse Ozaki said quietly: "Doctor, I have just heard that Dr. Miyazaki is getting worse."

The words shook him as he realized that he had all but forgotten about his injured colleague. Now, with all of the patients out of the hospital, and the others here as comfortable as he could make them, there was no reason why he could not leave at once to visit her.

He called to the seminary student, Noguchi, and together the two men set out toward the hill across the river where Dr. Miyazaki had been carried. As he walked across the scorched fields, Dr. Sakurai recalled jokingly telling the staffers the night before "not to get injured," because he was too sentimental to treat any of them who were so close to him. Now the finger had pointed at dear Dr. Miyazaki and he had no choice. One consolation was that Brother Mizuiwa, Mr. Noguchi and Nurse Ozaki had come through the ordeal unscathed.

"Here's the river, Doctor," Mr. Noguchi remarked as they

walked down a slight slope. The Motohara River runs some 600 yards beyond the hospital. Halfway up the hill behind it, there is a copse with a spring of cold water in the middle. For a hundred years or so, the residents of that area, their children and grandchildren, have called the spring the "Water of the Last Age." It is the custom to give that water to the critically ill.

When the two men reached the spring, they came upon a heartrending scene. There, squatting near the clear water, was the group of whitish, ghostlike people the doctor had seen earlier. Unable to stand their burning wounds and terrible thirst, they had come to drink of the Water of the Last Age. As he approached, they called out to him, begging for help. He saw many familiar faces, including some women from the nearby Cross Society Order who had been weeding in their fields at the moment of impact. He had no way of helping them, but he promised them he would return with medicine as soon as he could get it.

The two men entered the small grove of Japanese oaks just beyond. The air was cool and, as he squinted into the sudden darkness, he saw Dr. Miyazaki and the chief nurse lying on the ground.

"How are you both feeling?" he asked and was surprised to see them look up at him with an air of resentment, their eyes seeming to accuse him of neglecting them. The chief nurse's legs appeared only slightly burned, and he quickly switched his attention to Dr. Miyazaki. Her head had been bandaged and blood had soaked through. But it seemed to have stopped now. Still, she looked very pale, as though she had lost a lot of blood. He felt her pulse. It was even but very weak.

"I'm sorry I couldn't get here sooner. There were . . . so many . . . the injured people," he said helplessly.

Dr. Miyazaki's eyes softened immediately. "It was bad, wasn't it?" she asked weakly.

"Yes, very bad."

"The patients?"

"All safe and out of the hospital." He felt strangely proud to be able to inform her of that.

The chief nurse spoke abruptly, pointing at the abandoned building: "It's a good thing. The hospital is on fire."

"I know," he said. "Everything burns, but we have saved our own lives at least," he murmured, then instantly regretted the words. Dr. Miyazaki's condition was very serious and when he looked back at her he found her eyes on his, and she nodded slightly as if guessing his thoughts. Desperately, he wondered what he could do for her, but there was nothing he could do without medicine.

He heard a voice calling softly, and he turned and saw a man and a woman with a child on her back sitting on the ground a short distance away. He recognized Mr. Kinoshita and his wife and son, who lived near the hospital. "Can you help my husband, Doctor?" she called. He walked over to them. "What happened to you?" he asked.

Mr. Kinoshita, short, compact, and about 30 years old, was a teacher at Yamazato Primary School. That morning he, along with a few other teachers, had been digging in the school playground when the bomb exploded some 1,000 yards away from them. Though badly burned, Mr. Kinoshita was able to find his way to his house near Mt. Motohara. When he arrived, he found his house demolished and his family nowhere to be seen. A few minutes later, his wife found him, squatting helplessly on the ground. She told him that she had managed to get to a shelter and tried to comfort him, as he gasped and pleaded for water. Finally, she had led him to this little forest glade.

Now she did not know what else to do. "Can't we help him, Doctor?" she asked.

Pointing toward the hospital, Dr. Sakurai replied, "When that fire is out, I will try to get some medicine. I'm afraid you will have to wait until then. In the meantime, apply whatever oil you can find to his body."

"Should I let him eat these?" she asked, showing him a few cucumbers she had picked up on the farm.

"By all means, let him eat them if he can. They may give him some strength."

He stood up and called to Dr. Miyazaki and the chief nurse, "I'll be back. Try to rest."

Motioning for Mr. Noguchi to come with him, he headed toward the hospital. At the spring, he passed the same group of ghostlike people, only now some of them were dead. Once again, the feeling of helplessness assailed him. There was so very little that he could do.

CHAPTER 13

"Mayday! Mayday!"

1230 HOURS

SWEENEY WAS ASTONISHED THAT THEY WERE STILL AIRBORNE. A few minutes after leaving Nagasaki, he had asked Jimmy Van Pelt to give him the quickest course to Okinawa and the approximate distance. The navigator quickly gave him the bad news: By the most direct route, Okinawa was about 350 miles away. Sweeney's rapid mental calculations confirmed his fears. At 1600 rpms and 28 inches of manifold pressure, a B-29 consumes approximately 300 gallons of gasoline an hour. With their present weight and at normal speed, their fuel should run out about fifty miles short of Okinawa. Sweeney could only hope that their reduced speed and the lowering of the nose into a slight glide would conserve just enough fuel for them to make it. But he seriously doubted it.

Now by some miracle they were in sight of Okinawa and Yontan Field. For the last half-hour, Radioman Abe Spitzer had been trying to raise someone at the field, but all his messages had gone unanswered. As Sweeney approached Yontan, he could see the P-38s taking off and landing in a continuous stream. Well, they better get the hell out of the way, because he couldn't wait. He was coming in *now!*

Then Kuharek's voice was in his ear. "Skipper, as of right now, all the fuel gauges read empty. I don't know what we're flying on." As if to punctuate his statement, the right outboard engine suddenly coughed and faded.

"Increase power to number three engine," Sweeney said to Albury between tight lips. That did it! They would have no time either for a long, low approach or a wave-off from the field. And since they might well have to make a dead-stick landing, he had to aim for the halfway point on the runway. "We've got to get this damn thing down before we spin in," he said.

But the field was still ignoring them. Sweeney instructed Olivi and Van Pelt to fire flares, the red and green ones that were the colors for that day. But after four flares had burst in the air, the traffic pattern on the ground remained uninterrupted.

"Give me the field," he shouted. "*Bock's Car* calling Yontan Field. Mayday! Mayday!" He could hear the tower talking to other planes, but they were oblivious to him. "Mayday! Mayday!" he called over and over. No answer. Finally, in exasperation, he yelled, "I want any goddam tower on Okinawa."

When silence was the only response, he called back to Olivi and Van Pelt, "Fire off the flares."

"Which ones?" Olivi asked.

"Fire 'em all! Every goddam one!"

It must have startled observers on the ground to see the fireworks display that suddenly burst over the limping B-29. Twenty flares of all colors, signifying "heavy damage," "aircraft on fire," "dead and wounded on board," "aircraft out of fuel," "prepare for crash landing," dotted the sky. The effect was electric. Planes abruptly peeled away from the landing strip, and Sweeney could see fire trucks and ambulances racing toward the runway.

They were at 2,000 feet now and Sweeney shoved the wheel sharply forward. "We'll go right down," he said to Albury. "Tell the others to brace for a rough one."

They came in at 140 mph, about 30 mph too fast. The plane hit about halfway down the runway, bounced a good twenty-five feet in the air, and settled. At that moment, the port outboard engine quit and the plane veered sharply to the left, toward the line of B-24s at the edge of the runway. Sweeney immediately flicked the switch for the reversible props, newly installed on B-29s, and hit the emergency brakes, and the plane straightened and slowed. It finally rolled to a stop about ten feet short of the end of the runway.

Sweeney wiped the sweat from his forehead, turned to Albury, and flashed his exuberant Irish grin. "Just a routine flight, eh, pal?"

Said Albury, "I was never so damn glad to see the ground in all my life."

Later, Flight Engineer Kuharek measured the remaining fuel. He found that out of the 6,250 gallons of gasoline they had started with, not counting the useless trapped gallons, they had exactly seven gallons left in all tanks. Put in terms of the fuel tank of an automobile, that was the equivalent of *two teaspoonsful* of gasoline.

But they had made it. A minute later the door opened and a sergeant poked his head in. "Where are the dead and wounded?"

Sweeney looked at him. He suddenly felt a terrible tiredness. "Back there," he said. He was pointing to the northeast, toward Nagasaki.

For the last hundred minutes, Tsuneo Tomita, the third-year student at the Nagasaki Medical College, had been huddled deep inside the large shelter at the university, untouched, unhurt, but vastly shocked at the sight of his friends and colleagues tumbling into the cavelike shelter only to die. And for at least half an hour, an old Buddhist poem had been repeating itself over and over in his head: "We eat, excrete, sleep and get up. This is our world. All we have to do after that—is to die."

At first, it had been a routine morning of digging in the shelter, a morning like any other during the past three weeks. When Tomita had joined his fellow students at the medical school at nine o'clock, Professors Shimizu and Sugiura handed tools to the first six men in line, including Tomita, and told them to start digging deeper inside the shelter, to enlarge it. The young men, picking up hoes and picks and dirt-carrying baskets, had entered the cave and begun to work. All morning long they swung their picks and hoes, until about eleven o'clock when they were granted a break. Tomita's friends, Narasaki and Tanaka, immediately disappeared to find some water. Professor Sugiura had gone out earlier to talk to a reporter from the *Nishinippon Shimbun*. Tomita and the others had been content merely to sit and chat with Professor Shimizu, who had joined them after conducting his nine o'clock class.

Suddenly, Professor Shimizu held up his hand. "Hear the noise?" he had whispered. "Be quiet! Listen!" Gradually, Tomita was able to detect the distant drone of a B-29. Almost before the fact had registered, there was a light that permeated to the deepest part of the shelter, a roaring that seemed to come from the very bowels of the earth. Flung several feet away, his ears ringing, gasping for breath in the sudden vacuum, Tomita lay still and unbelieving.

An eternity later, someone called out hoarsely, "A plane

has crashed at the entrance of the shelter. It is blocked now. We will be buried alive."

The professor immediately shouted him down: "Everybody all right here? We're going to have to dig through the entrance right away. Make it snappy! Let's go!"

As students Ikeda and Kashiwa ran toward the entrance, Tomita stood up and felt a cool breeze coming from somewhere. "Professor," he called, "there must be an exit around here. I can feel air coming in." Then he looked toward the entrance and saw a shaft of light coming through a large hole. "We're all right," he yelled. "There is the opening. I can see it!"

But Kashiwa had already found it for himself and was peering outside. "Professor, something terrible has happened out there," he said in a strange voice. "The pine tree mountain has been turned into a brown hill of clay. The concrete walls around the campus are no longer there and some of the buildings have been smashed flat. People are lying on the ground everywhere. They look like mud dolls. Come and see for yourself."

"What are you talking about?" the professor cried and rushed toward the opening.

Tomita followed just in time to catch a man who came tumbling in through the hole, moaning, "I'm wounded. Oh, God. It hurts!" Tomita held him in his arms and looked at his face. He shuddered. Was this the face of a man? There was no hair on his head or above his eyes, the forehead and cheeks were inflamed beyond recognition, the lips blistered and peeling. With his entire body naked, burned and bloodstained, he looked like no creature of this earth.

Tomita blurted out, "Who are you? What's your name?"

The man stared at him and then closed his eyes in dismay. "Tomita," he gasped. "It is I, Matsumoto."

In his shock, Tomita almost dropped his injured friend. How could he have failed to recognize his classmate? But was this blackened wreck the once handsome Matsumoto? Yes, he could see it now. Gently, he lowered the other to the floor of the shelter. "I'm sorry, Matsumoto. So sorry."

"It was my own fault," the injured man panted. "When I saw the parachute falling out of the single B-29, it was so unusual that I stopped near the entrance to study it. That's the last thing I remember. He twisted convulsively on the floor. "Oh, Tomita," he whispered. "It hurts so. Can't you do something for me?"

"Get some rest," Tomita said softly. "I'll try to find some water." But before he could move, Professor Shimizu and Shiina came back in supporting other injured students. Tomita leaped to help, half-dragging the victims deeper inside the shelter one by one. He found that he could recognize most of them only by the most careful scrutiny. His classmates tried to stand the pain bravely, despite the peeled-off skin hanging from their arms and chests, the eyelids burned and stuck together so that they could barely open their eyes. There was Miyamoto, injured in the stomach and groaning, Murayama, who had been found unconscious at the entrance. He had been sipping water at the time and it was still in his mouth and nose. The two giants, Yoneda and Ejima, once they had been lowered to benches in the rear of the shelter, never moaned or complained of their grievous wounds, only looked upward with calm, untroubled faces.

It was already too late for Tanaka, who must have been killed in the first instant. A pitcher on the school baseball team, he was found still clutching the stone he carried to strengthen his hand. Watanabe, the fierce one, looked Tomita in the eye and said, "My friend, it is clear that man doesn't die very easily, isn't it?" Tomita was astonished that Watanabe, so severely injured, could find such beautiful words.

And there was the lifeless body of Tada, who alone had somehow known the day before that death was near, and whose presentiment had come all too terribly true. Finally, there was Ikeda who returned ashen-faced from an outside inspection, and was already beset by the invisible killer called radiation. He announced that he would lead eleven classmates up Mt. Anakobo—to safety. None was ever heard from again.

A short time later, Shiina cried: "The fires are raging outside and they are getting very close to the shelter. If we stay here any longer we'll be steamed to death. Let's get away quickly." But Tomita, unhurt as he was, could not bear to leave those less fortunate than he to make what he considered a cowardly retreat. "No, I'll stay. You go if you want to. Besides, my house must have been destroyed. There's no place for me to go."

Shiina looked hard at him, then nodded in resignation. The two friends shook hands, and Shiina disappeared into the smoke. Tomita would never see him again.

Shortly after his friend had departed, Tomita was startled by the noise of burning timber crashing about the entrance of the shelter, blocking it. Instantly, a heat wave swept into the cave, filling it with smoke and ashes. He ripped off part of his loincloth, tore off a piece, wet it with the water from a small jar and covered his nose and mouth with it. Then he remoistened the cloth and went from one injured student to another, providing what comfort he could.

Professor Shimizu had begun to clear away the debris from the entrance when Tomita heard him cry out. He rushed to the professor and found that a length of burning timber had crashed down on the older man's back. He pushed it off, and the professor rolled over on his side, moaning, "I'm done, Tomita. Do everything possible after I'm gone. Go to the hospital if you can and get help." With that, he lost consciousness, and as the young man realized that he was the only one left whole in the shelter he panicked.

"Professor, don't pass out!" he cried. "Don't leave me alone with the dying! What shall I do?" But then, quickly, reason returned. He moved the professor away from the entrance and put a wet cloth on his burned back.

What could have happened outside to have caused this agony? Tomita moved to the entrance and tried to see through the debris. It looked as if the flames had turned away from the shelter and the wind had lost its strength. But there was not a living creature left in the desolation around them. Only here in this shelter did life exist, and that was flickering.

He walked back to find that the professor had regained consciousness. Now he stood up weakly, peering toward the entrance. "Tomita, the fires apparently have died down outside. The glow is gone from the entrance. I must make a report to the hospital as soon as possible and try to get some help for our friends here. I sent Kashiwa, but he has not yet returned. He may well have been swallowed by the flames. We shall have to go ourselves."

Tomita nodded, although he glanced back at the still forms lying on the floor. Yes, it would be better to go and get some kind of help—if there was such a thing as "help" in what he guessed must be a ravaged city. To protect themselves from the fire, both men coated their bodies with dirt.

It was a full two hours after the man-made earthquake that Tomita had his first look at the outside world, and it was an appalling sight. Beyond the ruins of Yamazato, Shiroyama and Matsuyama schools, the bald mountains of Inasayama smoldered. Nearby, the beautiful cedar groves that had sheltered their dugout were no longer there. Although the trees had been over a foot in diameter, every one of them had been cut down as if by a giant scythe some two feet above the ground. The sun was partially obscured in the dust-filled sky.

Tomita began hopping up and down, the scorching-hot earth painful to the soles of his bare feet. The professor smiled wanly at the sight, and without a word the two men stumbled away over nails and glass splinters toward the ruins of the Nagasaki Medical College.

Near the administration building, they could see the various objects scattered all around—punctured helmets, bits of clothing, a woman's slashed white shoes. The three wards of the hospital were engulfed by fire, and other buildings, too, were tumbling down in flaming wreckage.

The professor looked at his student with red-rimmed eyes. "Tomita, the way things look from here no one in the hospital could have been saved."

Before Tomita could reply, a middle-aged man came over the top of a nearby hill. The professor called out, "Have you seen any of the University Hospital doctors and nurses?"

The man paused and scratched his head. He was short and broad and a dirty white bandage covered one of his arms from elbow to shoulder. "The hospital people? They have gone to the mountain over there," he answered, pointing to the east. "There is a flag near them."

"Thank you very much," the professor shouted, and murmured to Tomita with great emotion, "It is incredible! Some must still be alive!"

The two men walked quickly toward the east until they came to a steep hill. Near the top, at the edge of a large, burned-out sweet-potato patch, Tomita came to a sudden standstill and his heart nearly stopped. Before him lay what must have been close to 500 people, naked, squirming with pain, moaning. There was a mother breast-feeding her baby without realizing that it had already died, her one breast covered with glass splinters. Beside her were two teen-age girls lying with their arms clasped about each other in the throes of death. Nearby, an old woman stared at the stump where her foot had been, while blood welled out from beneath the makeshift tourniquet. People called frantically for sons, husbands, mothers.

On the far side of the clearing a white flag, held aloft by a student with bandaged head, flapped against the sky. As Tomita approached he saw that the Rising Sun had been drawn in blood, and he wondered for an instant whose blood it had been.

Professor Shimizu had located Dean Tsunoo among the survivors and, grabbing Tomita's arm, he picked his way to where the gentle old man stood, and gave him a report on the pharmacy section. Though extremely pale in the face and bleeding from the head, the dean looked composed and assured as always. Forty-eight hours later he would be dead. Standing alongside of him, Tomita saw, was Professor Shirabe of the surgery department. A handsome, capable doctor, Shirabe was peering closely at the swarm of injured, trying to spot those people who could still be helped. But most were beyond help.

Professor Shimizu had finished his recitation and the dean nodded in understanding. "Take care of your students," he said in a weak voice. "They are the ones who matter."

The professor nodded in return. "Yes. Of course, we will. But do you think someone might be sent to help?"

The dean looked slowly around him at the dying and the dead. "We'll try," he said. "As you can see, we have our problems here, too."

The professor and Tomita, at the dean's words, turned toward each other, each remembering the friends back in the shelter. Without further delay they hurried back to their own particular injured and dying. No sound came from the shelter as they approached, and the silence alarmed them. Inside, they found their fears justified; some were already dead, and none of the living had strength to yell. The professor told Tomita: "See if you can find some water outside."

The young man ran to the water tank beside the shelter. The cover of the large wooden tank was open and when he peered inside he saw the bodies of two students floating face down. Still, the tank was almost full and, without hesitating, he scooped up some water with his helmet. His friends couldn't know where it had come from. They drank and drank as if they would never be able to get enough. Mad with joy, they drank helmetsful without stopping for breath and asked for more, please, more. As Tomita journeyed back and forth to the tank, his own salt tears mixed with the contaminated water.

A little while later, two nurses, probably sent by the dean, visited the shelter, examined each of the survivors, and gave several of them injections. The rest, they said with little surprise, were lost. Under the circumstances, that was all they could do.

In the evening, Tomita left the shelter for a breath of air. On the high hill nearby, the ruins of the Urakami Cathedral still burned. The district where he lived too, was being consumed by flames. He had little doubt that his mother and brothers were dead.

Inside the shelter it was finally quiet. He and the professor lay down on the mud floor. It had become cold and Tomita shivered. But there was one blessing: The bugs were gone. The mosquitoes that usually swarmed during the evening must have lost their wings.

The next morning, he and the professor carried the surviving students out of the shelter. There were only two. Yoneda, Ejima, Murayama and Watanabe had died during the night. Tomita remembered Watanabe's words: "Man doesn't die very easily." Perhaps not easily, he thought, but with great finality.

In the distance, two people were coming in their direction, calling, "Mr. Matsumoto. Mr. Matsumoto." The couple, it turned out, were the husband and wife who had been boarding Matsumoto at their home. They had become very fond of the young man, and they had brought a shopping basket full of fruit, eggplants and cucumbers for him. But food held no interest for poor Matsumoto, who was already talking incoherently in his high fever. The couple tried to comfort him, and Matsumoto seemed to sense their presence, for he came out of his delirium long enough to smile faintly and hold their hands. Half an hour after they arrived, he suddenly cried out: "Mother, Mother. *Banzai!*" Then he died. Slowly the couple trudged off over the hill.

With Matsumoto gone, Okamoto who had reeled into the dugout early in the previous afternoon, was the lone survivor. He staggered about apparently searching for a place to die. He whispered to Tomita, "Tomita, stay with me until I die. I don't want to be alone." When he collapsed, Tomita sat beside him and offered his left arm as a pillow. He tried to use his own body to shield his friend from the sun, but Okamoto, unable to lie still, kept twisting to the right and left. Finally, he gasped, "Tomita, where are you? I can't see you anymore. Just the shadow of your face. Oh, I want to see my parents before I die. If you come across my mother, give her this . . . this watch. Ah." His arm dropped and he lay still with his eyes still open. Tomita's heart was frozen.

Later that morning, he and the professor cremated the other students—the friends with whom Tomita had studied and worked for so long—in front of the shelter. Tomita built a little wooden marker for each, inscribed each friend's name in charcoal. Then the young man and the professor saluted the ashes in a final farewell.

Looking at the markers in a row on the ground, Tomita was overcome with sadness. More than a thousand years ago a man had written:

The voice of the waves
    That rise before me
Is not so loud
    As my weeping,
That I am left behind.

CHAPTER 14

The Other "Bomb"

1305 HOURS

JUST AFTER ONE O'CLOCK, THERE WAS A TELEPHONE CALL FOR Mr. Gunji Kitamura, the chief of production at the Isahaya airplane factory, some fifteen miles from Nagasaki.

"*Moshi, moshi* (yes, go ahead)," he said impatiently. How the devil was he supposed to increase production if he was constantly being interrupted?

The caller was Mr. Endo, the parts supervisor. "Mr. Kitamura," he said, "could you possibly come down to the research laboratory?"

"What is it? What's wrong now?"

"They have brought in a strange object."

"Strange object? What kind of object? What does it look like?"

"Forgive me, it looks very much like—a bomb."

"I'll be right there." He hung up, thoughtful. What now? Then he set off briskly. Much out of the ordinary had been happening lately, and he had the feeling that nothing could surprise him very much anymore—not even a bomb.

Until a few months ago, Mr. Kitamura had been working near the Omura Air Base, but Omura had been damaged so heavily by bombing that he and some of his men had been transferred to a branch factory at Isahaya, which was closely surrounded by mountains and was therefore considered almost bombproof. It needed to be, if they were to resume full production. Technically, production was already in full swing that summer of 1945, but Mr. Kitamura and a few other top people realized what a hollow phrase that was. The dwindling supply of materials, the pitiful condition of returned aircraft, the almost total lack of parts with which to repair them, told him how badly the war was really going for Japan. He considered the recent invasion and fall of Okinawa only a blueprint of what lay in store for the main islands—invasion and total defeat—unless the war was brought to a speedy end.

That was more than just a guess. Mr. Kitamura had access to a piece of information known to only a handful of people at the aircraft factory. That very morning, he had seen top-secret documents, flown to the factory from military intelligence headquarters, which described the bomb just used at Hiroshima as "extremely powerful and accompanied by terrific heat rays which could burn the skin most severely." It was not known at that time, the documents revealed, exactly how the bomb had been made, only that it had been dropped by parachute and had caused the deaths of a great many people. Top management was urged to disregard any rumors to the effect that such a weapon could affect Japan's capacity to wage war. On the contrary, "the determination of the people to defend their very homes has never been more evident than now." And they, the executives of the factory, must see to it that aircraft production was not only maintained, but actually increased to meet the new threat.

The threat, particularly to Nagasaki, had been made clear by the Americans themselves. Just the day before, someone had brought him a leaflet dropped by one of the B-29 planes, warning the people of the city to leave quickly, because Nagasaki would very soon "be turned into a city of ashes and death." Mr. Kitamura was inclined to believe that warning.

Still, it was a surprise when it actually happened. It was about eleven o'clock and he had been explaining an assembly procedure to a group of the Student Patriotic Corps. Right in the middle of a sentence there was a great *Thunk!* as if someone had dropped a very large melon on the roof. Seconds later came a sudden, strong wind, a gentle rumbling, then silence. Mr. Kitamura dropped the tool he had been holding and ran outside. The sky was empty; there was no airplane anywhere in sight. When he looked around, he saw that there had been no explosion here, no damage.

He was about to return to the building when he saw a gigantic column of smoke rising behind a hill in the direction of Nagasaki. A young man ran to him from the office building shouting: "Mr. Kitamura, news has just come from the air defense observation post at Shiroyama in the city that some kind of monster bomb was just dropped on Nagasaki."

"What else did they say?" he asked. "How great was the damage? How many planes attacked?"

"We don't know. The report stopped all at once and we haven't heard one more word."

"Well, we can't do anything about it, I suppose. We had better get back to work. We still have airplanes to build."

The young man smiled a little worriedly. "Yes, I know. But, sir?" He hesitated.

"What is it?"

"Do you think it might be some kind of special bomb, or maybe a large attack by many airplanes?"

"I don't know." But he was almost certain that he did know.

When he reached the research laboratory and entered, he

saw a small group of people—one or two of his assistant managers and a few lab technicians—clustered around a table. He called a greeting and they made way for him as he approached. Suddenly he stopped. Lying flat on the table in front of him was a metal bomb, or at least it appeared to be a bomb. It was about five feet long and one and a half feet in diameter. Mr. Kitamura had seen many bombs during his career but nothing quite like this one. It looked like an ugly, bloated cucumber.

The other men were silent, staring at him, waiting for him to do something. Everybody wants the top job, he thought. But when it comes to acting like the top man, no one wants the responsibility.

"Where the devil did this thing come from?" he asked.

"It was picked up in a field near Uki, Mr. Kitamura," said Mr. Endo, his parts supervisor. "They say that it was dropped from a B-29 at about the same time as the . . . other bomb, and that a parachute was attached to it."

Mr. Kitamura stood studying the ugly thing, wondering whether any sort of timing mechanism had been set and was even now clicking its way toward detonation. He walked closer and bent over, staring at the metal object. There seemed to be about a dozen small holes punched around the covering, and, as he squinted through one of them, he thought he could see another object inside. Could that be the explosive charge? He didn't think so. He suspected that this was not a bomb at all. He put his ear next to the metal skin, listening intently, and heard a distinct, steady ticking, like a miniature metronome. Now he wasn't so sure. Maybe it was a bomb.

He stood up quickly and turned to face the others. "Something—I don't know what—has been activated inside," he informed them. "I have to take the thing apart—now, without further delay. It may be dangerous, so I suggest that you all leave and wait outside." He was not very surprised to see the alacrity with which the others took up his suggestion, scampering toward the doorway—and safety. He didn't blame them. Only Mr. Endo remained, his sad eyes fixed on his chief's face. "I'll stay, if I may, sir. You may need some help."

Mr. Kitamura nodded, grateful for the company and moral support, and bent to the task before him. He reached out a hand and touched the metal cover; it was very warm. He took a deep breath, grasped the object firmly, and rolled it slightly toward his side of the table so that he could work on it more easily. His action had exposed the left side of the cylinder, and he saw that a long vertical rudder, with four small wings attached, ran along that side toward the rear. It looked less and less like a bomb. The use of the parachute supported the possibility he had in mind: that this casing contained something other than explosives—something perhaps more delicate.

Scrutinizing the "bomb," he noticed a cap at the back end near the rudder. If he were lucky, it would be a screw-type cap with no detonating wires attached. If he were wrong . . . Well, neither of them would know very much about anything anymore.

"Will you hold the thing, Mr. Endo? I want to see if this cap unscrews."

While Mr. Endo grasped the cylinder with both hands, Mr. Kitamura began turning the cap. To his surprise it came off easily. He removed it and saw the plain white envelope sticking to the inside cover. He leaned over and peered inside the cylinder.

"What do you see, Mr. Kitamura?" Mr. Endo asked anxiously. "What is inside?"

"Instruments," he answered quickly. "Dozens of tiny instruments. I don't think there's anything to be afraid of."

"But what are the instruments used for?"

Mr. Kitamura thought for a moment. "It's just a guess,

but I have a hunch they were used to measure the effect of the new bomb. Several of them are still running. That was the noise we heard."

He picked up the cover and gently separated the envelope from it, staring at the unfamiliar words. He was able to make out a name: "To Professor Sagane," and there was a letter inside. His knowledge of English, however, was very limited and he decided to call in the others waiting outside. Perhaps their combined efforts could unravel the fiendish English language.

Soon, they were all crowding around, asking questions. He told them what he had found and what he suspected the "bomb" really was, then asked if anyone had ever heard of a "Professor Sagane."

"Oh, yes," said one of the lab technicians quickly. "He was one of my teachers at Tokyo University—a professor of physics."

Half an hour later they had succeeded in translating the letter. It read:

Headquarters
Atomic Bomb Command
August 9, 1945

To: PROF. F. SAGANE

From: Three of your former scientific colleagues during your stay in the United States.

We are sending this as a personal message to urge you to use your influence as a reputable nuclear physicist to convince the Japanese General Staff of the terrible consequences which will be suffered by your people if you continue in this war.

You have known for several years that an atomic bomb could be built if a nation were willing to pay the enormous cost of preparing the necessary material. Now that you have seen that we have constructed the production plants, there can be no doubt in your mind that all the output of these factories, working twenty-four hours a day, will be exploded on your homeland.

Within the space of three weeks, we have proof-fired one bomb in the American desert, exploded one in Hiroshima and fired the third this morning.

We implore you to confirm these facts to your leaders and to do your utmost to stop the destruction and waste of life which can only result in the total annihilation of your cities if continued. As scientists, we deplore the use to which a beautiful discovery has been put, but we can assure you that unless Japan surrenders at once, this rain of atomic bombs will increase manyfold in fury.

Mr. Kitamura stood holding the letter for a long time. This brief message, written not by a politician or a military man, but by American scientists ten thousand miles away to an enemy who was still a fellow scientist, touched him deeply. It was a communication from human beings to another human being and it expressed what they all wanted: An end to the war. He felt tears scald his eyes. For he knew now that this also meant an end of the Japanese Empire, which had never lost a war before. They could expect no mercy now, for they had been the ones who started it all.

That evening, he climbed the hill and sat down staring at the distant fires still raging in Nagasaki. He felt a sense of hopelessness. If only some good could come out of this war and all the killing, he thought. If only it were the start of something, not the finish. But what?

Two weeks later, his question would be answered when Professor Sagane, who had come to evaluate the situation and, incidentally, to pick up his letter, spoke to some of the people at the factory. He told them that he had once discussed the feasibility of producing nuclear energy with an American scientist before the war, and both men had agreed that uranium offered the best possibility. After his return home, he had discussed the idea of making such a bomb in Japan, but the military had scoffed at the idea. He had concluded his speech with the words: "We have endured much, but I am convinced that this new energy will be used now to preserve the peace. Perhaps our suffering has served a purpose after all. So, please, have strength for the future."

Years afterward, Mr. Kitamura would write to a dear friend: "I will never forget Professor Sagane's words on that bleak and lonely day. They gave the light of hope to our empty hearts."

1500 HOURS

SHE WAS DYING, HE THOUGHT, AND THERE WAS NOTHING HE could do about it. She was the last one, and as he held her in his arms, he was suddenly afraid. What in the name of God had happened? But there was no one to provide the answer—only the girl's quick gasping as she tried to hold on to life . . .

Mr. Minoru Nakamura had been very busy that morning trying to handle his two jobs. The first was serving as paymaster for the accounting section of the Mitsubishi Arms Factory, which had been moved to the Shiroyama Primary School for the summer recess. His other job was to supervise the construction of bomb shelters for the 150 workers in the large school building—the clerical workers of Mitsubishi, the young male and female members of the Student Patriotic Corps, and the various teachers assigned there that summer. It was a big responsibility for the broad-shouldered, handsome 23-year-old Nakamura, and it had so far kept him exempt from military service.

When the air-raid alarm had sounded a little earlier, Mr. Nakamura realized that in his second job he had been derelict in his duties. There was room enough in the shelters for barely half the people there; the others had to stand outside. He decided to enlarge the shelters without further delay. After the all-clear, he organized the people into twenty-man groups, which would take turns digging in the shelters that day.

The first shift of diggers, including Mr. Nakamura himself, had been digging inside the shelter when the electric light bulb in the miner's torch hanging overhead had burst and a second later he had been blown off his feet. Since he had been deepest inside the cave at the moment, he had to climb over sprawled bodies to reach the entrance. There, shovel still in hand, he climbed outside into the heat and carnage.

He could see very little at first; the dust from the sweet-potato patch that had once been the school playground swirled about madly. At last, he was able to make out shapes, and the first thing he noticed was that the huge mound of dirt that had been built in front of the shelter for additional protection had been smashed flat. As the dust began to settle, he could see how the world around him had altered. There, lying on the sweet-potato patch, were dozens of burned corpses. No trees had been left standing. The whole area had turned gray; all the green had been instantly wiped away. All the windows and window frames in the school had been punched inward. The second- and third-floor roofs had collapsed.

Even as he was wondering whether anyone within the building had survived, he saw students jumping out of empty windows or rushing through gaping doorways or holes in the wall. Many had been injured by flying objects, or partly crushed beneath concrete and wood, and were bleeding and clutching damaged limbs. He heard the cries from inside and hurried to the building to see if he could help anyone still trapped. Just inside the front entrance, he came upon three teen-age girls lying dazed and terrified, but apparently not seriously injured. He carried them to the shelter. The last one, a 17-year-old girl named Natsue, asked, "Mr. Nakamura, what happened? Did a bomb hit the school?"

Nakamura could give no answer; he had no idea himself. There was no sign, no crater, which should have been left had a bomb fallen nearby. Yet all the other signs pointed to some great explosion. He quickly climbed the hill under which the shelter had been constructed, and saw that all the structures in the entire Shiroyama district had been squashed flat and were burning fiercely.

He returned to the shelter, afraid now that what had happened had been terrible beyond his comprehension. He had to report what had happened here to the main Ohashi office. As he was about to leave the shelter and start out, a group of about eight girls including the three he had rescued, all members of the Patriotic Corps, came up and asked if they could come along with him. They were anxious to reach their homes in the Shiroyama district. He could not bear to tell them that he thought they had no homes. Instead, he merely nodded. He noticed that Natsue's glasses had been broken, and he reached out and gently removed the shattered frames from her nose. "Come along," he said softly to her, taking her by the hand.

Together, he and the girls started toward the center of the neighborhood, but their way was soon blocked by fire. They must circle the area by way of Mt. Shiroyama and approach it from the north. After a half hour of walking, the girls were complaining of a terrible thirst, but there was no water anywhere. Perhaps it had evaporated.

As they climbed higher on the mountain, the girls began to look back toward the devastation. They cried out, "Look, my whole neighborhood is on fire." Or, "My house has been destroyed." Or, "My whole family must be dead." Natsue, still holding Nakamura's hand, put her other hand up before her face as if to blot out the sight. "There is nothing left," she whispered. "Nothing can still be alive."

Soon they came to a spring near the top of Mt. Shiroyama. Nakamura called a halt; the girls were obviously exhausted and needed to rest. He told them: "You girls rest here until I get back from the Ohashi plant." They sank gratefully to the ground and began drinking from the spring. Only Natsue continued to regard him with sad eyes.

"Do you have to go now, Mr. Nakamura?" she asked.

"Yes. I must report what happened and try to get some help."

"I don't want you to go."

"It will be all right. You wait here. I'll be back. I promise." With that he turned and hurried down the slope. When he looked back he saw that she was still staring after him.

He walked swiftly toward the Ohashi factory, trying to ignore the dazed and wounded people he encountered. Halfway there he saw a boy of about 18 sandwiched between two fallen pillars at the Mitsubishi Electric Company. Nakamura could see glass splinters all over his bare chest and stomach. On seeing Nakamura, the boy cried, "Help me, please." Nakamura took hold of his arms and managed to pull him out from between the timbers.

He turned to leave but the boy detained him. "Please, don't go. I can't see anything with my right eye."

Nakamura looked closely and spotted a thin piece of glass, about a half inch long, stuck in his right eye. He pinched it between thumb and forefinger and gently pulled it out. The boy uttered not a word—no cry, no sound of complaint. Nakamura helped him rise and guided him to a shady place. "I'm on the way to get a rescue party," he told him. "Stay here until we come back to pick you up." The boy nodded, but he was gone when Nakamura passed that way again.

He was stunned to find that the Ohashi factory, too, was in flames and almost totally destroyed. For a moment, he couldn't think what to do next. He had come here to get a rescue party, only to find ruins. Apparently, those still alive had fled to shelters. There was no one left to report to. Then he remembered the girls waiting for his return. He turned toward Mt. Shiroyama and began to walk swiftly.

When he reached the spring on Mt. Shiroyama, there were three girls there. Two, he saw at once, were already dead, though from what he could not imagine, for they had not been badly burned. Only Natsue, her eyes fixed on some distant point over the horizon, was still alive. He sat down on the ground beside her. "Are you all right?"

Her head swiveled slowly toward him and she smiled weakly. "I knew you would come back, Mr. Nakamura. The other girls said you would never return and they left. But you promised, and so I waited for you."

She began to tremble, and he asked, "Can I help you? Can I get you anything?"

"I'm cold, so cold." Her trembling increased until her teeth chattered. "Would you . . . could you . . . hold me, Mr. Nakamura? Hold me in your arms?"

He put his arms around her. "You'll be all right now."

"I want to go home," she whispered. "My eyes . . . I can't see very well."

"Take it easy. See! I'm holding you in my arms."

"I feel so sleepy."

She began to droop and Nakamura squeezed her roughly. "No! Stay awake!" he cried. "I will not let you drift away. Hold on! Hold on tight to me." She held tight, whispering, "Mother, Mother."

Then slowly, very slowly, Nakamura felt her arms slacken their hold. Her head slipped sideways and rested on his shoulder. He looked down and saw her hand slowly come unclenched, and relax on the ground, palm upward, the fingers curled over ever so slightly.

Still, he held her tightly. He could not let her go.

Her name was Natsue, which means "summer." He held Natsue tightly, and the tears rolled down his face.

CHAPTER 15

Up from the Ashes

1700 HOURS

FOR OVER HALF A DAY, POLITICAL AND BUSINESS LEADERS IN Nagasaki had been trying to cope with the immense problems created by the "new-type" bomb. Each had been striving to bring some order, some relief, to the stricken city. And each, traveling along a different road, had already played an important part in the rehabilitation process.

At five o'clock, the governor called a conference in Air Defense Headquarters to discuss emergency rescue procedures. Governor Nagano turned first to the man sitting on his right. "Mr. Mizogoshi, would you please give us your brief report?"

Mr. Genshiro Mizogoshi, the chief of the prefectural air defense section in Nagasaki, stood up and began speaking: "Mr. Governor, since the injured people must be our first concern, I have concentrated my efforts on them. Medical personnel and facilities have been hard-hit. Most of the hospitals have been destroyed and many doctors and medical students have been either killed or wounded. Therefore, I have sent messengers to various districts to seek the help of every practicing physician. I have also contacted by wireless the hospitals at Kyushu and Kumamoto universities and the naval hospital at Sasebo and asked them for additional medical personnel."

He looked down at the words he had scribbled, then continued. "Both gas plants have been destroyed and all trolley service halted because of damage to streetcars and deaths among conductors. Both Nagasaki and Urakami stations were demolished, but I understand that limited railroad service from Michinoo to the north has been re-established. Though the water stations are still functioning, there have been several main-line breaks and thousands of feeder-line breaks, so that getting enough water is a problem. Also, the loss of personnel and power has rendered many of the other service facilities inoperative. Fortunately, the phone company has an adequate supply of reserve wire. Its battery power will last for another seventy-two hours until electric power has been at least partially restored. I have been informed that teams of linemen have been dispatched to various important points within the city and are even now laying new lines on the ground as they go, until poles can be erected. We are trying to restore the fire-fighting units to full operation, since fire, particularly from individual stoves, is a major problem. It seems that much of the old city, and that means, of course, the seat of government, has not been severely damaged. We should have things under full control within three days."

There were murmurs of surprise from the others, who had not expected such a quick restoration. Then Mr. Mizogoshi turned to the bad news. "I have personally inspected the area as far north as Urakami Station and can attest to the fact that damage in that entire area is intense.

Most structures have been destroyed and fires rage everywhere. The streets are littered with tile, bricks, stone, corrugated iron and plaster—and corpses. Throughout the devastated area, all wounded have to be removed by stretcher, since no motor vehicles can traverse the streets." He sighed heavily and sat down. Then, the governor turned to Mr. Keiichi Ogawa, the chief of the Nagasaki office of the Kyushu Electric Company, and asked him to report. He rose quickly. "Electric power distribution and transmission systems have been totally disrupted." His next terse words were directed at Commander Matsuura of the Regiment District Military Police. "I expect to have one-third of our city lighted within a few hours. But I need help from the military. We are grateful for the few sailors who were dispatched from the naval station, but that is a drop in the bucket."

At that point, the MP chief began to object, arrogantly refusing to send soldiers on a "minor civilian mission." Ogawa, a burly, no-nonsense man, shouted him down: "Soon there will be lights in our city! And who will be responsible? The military? Never! The people will have done it. But your men can help us. The military—indeed everyone—should be grateful to the Kyushu Electric Company workers for what they have done so far. But the repairs are not going fast enough. Why can't you send us more soldiers?"

The others present were astonished, for in so challenging military authority, Mr. Ogawa was literally taking his life in his hands. But Ogawa did it without thinking. If he had stopped to consider, he might have held off. On the other hand, he might have decided, as had many others at that point, that it was now too late for the "old way" of thinking, the militaristic tradition of obedience and submission. Of what consequence, he might have wondered, was a charge of "insubordination" and "disloyalty" at this perilous point?

The governor had listened to the argument in silence.

Now he raised his hand and passed judgment. "As chairman of this conference, I order the military police commander to cooperate with Mr. Ogawa." The MP chief was dumbfounded at the decision. Then, when he realized that absolute authority no longer prevailed, he nodded his head in resignation. A new weapon had produced a new tradition.

Mr. Ogawa left the meeting satisfied. Six hours earlier, when the explosion had rendered his city powerless, Mr. Ogawa had reacted swiftly and professionally. For Ogawa was a true "wire man," part of that rare breed who consider their association with electricity both a duty and a pleasure. When the power failed, he became a man with a mission—and one not to be denied. Years earlier, when he had been a boy, an earthquake had struck the city where he lived and he had seen the effects of a power blackout on his fellow citizens: People already stunned and afraid had just about given up hope because of their terror in the total darkness, their sense of utter isolation. He intended to spare his neighbors in this city as much of that kind of suffering as he could.

Throughout the day, as reports of the extent of the damage came trickling into the main office, Ogawa sent people to try to bind up the shattered system, at least temporarily. But it was a massive repair job, with both generative sources and transmission lines inoperative. Both the Senza and the Takenokubo transformers had been knocked out. When he asked how bad it was, his assistant investigated and returned with an estimate: It would take at least three days to get the transformers in operation.

"Too long!" he snapped. "Do it in twelve hours."

Often repair was impossible. For example, the entire Urakami transformer station had been wiped out. "Don't bother with it then," he ordered. "Try to bypass to Sasebo for additional power." And it had been done.

Bad news kept coming in. A repairman, his face black and the skin peeling from his arms, staggered to Ogawa's office. "In Urakami and some neighboring districts, nearly all the electric poles have been snapped off," he had said, "and those that are still standing are on fire and out of order." Slowly and with great effort, the man gave a detailed report of where and how bad the damage was. When his report was finished, he collapsed. Mr. Ogawa was proud of him, as he had the competence and dedication of every true "wire man." Although this employee had been grievously wounded, he had made the effort to see with his own eyes the condition of his company and to report to his superiors. That was a professional job, thought Ogawa.

At three that afternoon, the fire at the prefecture hall swept toward the Kyushu Electric Company building. In the face of this new threat, members of the staff, mostly women, joined in the fire-fighting operation. Despite the fact that many outsiders had taken refuge in the concrete office building, it was the company women who, in the midst of caring for and feeding the refugees, had fought off the dangerous fire. Mr. Ogawa was satisfied. Because of their efforts, the vital wire in the warehouse had been saved and could still be used for reconstruction.

Then, there was his brief appearance at the governor's conference. Later that night, he stood by while a roll call was taken of the sweat-smeared, hollow-eyed staff. Twenty-one of the company's ninety employees had been killed, and the majority of those surviving had been injured to some extent. But no one had left, had abandoned his responsibility. Mr. Ogawa told them proudly, "You have done *some* job, let me tell you. But we must continue with our work. That is the mission that has been placed on our shoulders." And the others, deathly tired and worried about their families, accepted the challenge. Six hours later, half of all electric power had been restored to the downtown section.

Early next morning, employees loaded trucks with equipment and, together with a number of young sailors and soldiers, drove to the center of the bomb explosion. There, poles were quickly erected and wires began to link them. By midafternoon, the Saga-Isahaya main transmission lines were connected with the Egawa transformer station at Fukabori, and power for the entire Omura district in the city was turned on. Nagasaki was no longer broken up into isolated pockets of loneliness. That evening, the NHK broadcasting station went on the air.

Work proceeded around the clock, and by the evening of August 11, the entire city area was supplied with power. Lights were seen for the first time in certain parts of the bleak A-bombed desolation. It was the first overt sign of life in a dead land. As the lights flashed on, Mr. Ogawa's eyes shone. His men paused and stared at what they had accomplished. Even the soldiers, some of whom had cooperated only reluctantly, were awed.

Ten days later, Mr. Ogawa heard the words of his Emperor: "My people, you have lived under the blanket of total blackout, have surely suffered in that darkness of despair. But now, I can tell you to light your lamps bright so that you may have at last what little comfort is left in life."

On that night, lamps were lit in the windows of every home throughout the length and breadth of the ravaged land. They were the lights of peace.

The third man to speak at the governor's conference was Mr. Toyoshima, chief of the Rescue Corps. Mr. Toyoshima rose slowly and looked at the other members. "I concur with Mr. Mizogoshi's estimate of the enormous damage inflicted. I have traveled by patrol boat up the Urakami River as far as Takenobuko where we landed. To the north, the river was filled with bodies like so many dead fish floating on the surface. Near Takenobuko, many houses were on fire, and the streets were strewn with dead cats, dogs, horses and people. I am now certain that the Urakami district was the exact center of the explosion. Right now, treatment of the injured is imperative. We have been able to remove a large quantity of medicines from the burning prefectural building and have sent them to the rescue centers in Shinoyozen, Katsuyama and Yamazoto primary schools."

The governor nodded. "It is well. But I suggest that you go as soon as possible to the center of the explosion and, working outward, try and rescue any injured and clear the streets of the corpses. Because of the heat, it is imperative that this be done quickly."

So it was that in the next forty-eight hours, Mr. Toyoshima was in charge of one of the most grisly jobs ever assigned anyone—removing and cremating the thousands of dead inhabitants of Nagasaki. He soon found that one of the main problems was identifying the victims. Although people were supposed to wear a tag on their right breast bearing their name, address and blood type, a great many dead had no tags, and the condition of the bodies made it impossible to identify them. They were simply cremated as "unknowns."

To help with this odious job, workers were recruited from the Mitsubishi Shipyards. Mr. Toyoshima asked the chief of security to find him a large quantity of sake for emergency reasons. The chief sent over a sixteen-gallon barrel which was stored in Defense Headquarters. To give the workers the strength to endure their awful task, Mr. Toyoshima allowed each a glass of sake both before and after their time in the field. He thought it quite possible that the sake kept many of them sane.

For Mr. Toyoshima, there were moments of great anguish.

In a small shelter near Ibonokuchi, he discovered a family of four—the mother, a boy of 12, a 9-year-old girl, and a boy of about 6. They had not been burned, but, terrified of the world outside the shelter, they were determined to stay where they were. Mr. Toyoshima somehow felt personally responsible for their well-being. Those high in authority usually just give orders; here was a chance for him as an individual to salvage a bit of life. Whenever he could squeeze out a half hour from his frantic schedule, he would visit this family, taking food and water along. The children awaited him anxiously, crowding around to ask, "What have you brought this time, Uncle Police?"

But within twenty-four hours, two of the older children had inexplicably collapsed and could only stare at him weakly as he propped up their heads and tried to feed them. Perhaps they just needed rest, he thought. But on his next visit, they were both dead, and now the mother looked dazed and lifeless. He couldn't understand it. There was hardly a mark on them. He tried to comfort the woman, and gave the little boy a present, a wooden doll he had found in the streets.

The following afternoon, the little boy appeared before him at Defense Headquarters. "Mother died." His voice was firm, his chin high. "I'm all alone now and I want you to take me with you," he said with the terrible directness of the very young. "Mother gave me some money. Here." And he held up his dirty hand with several coins in it. The other clutched the doll that Mr. Toyoshima had given him.

Mr. Toyoshima reached out and closed the tiny fist with his great hand. "You keep the money," he said softly. "I *want* you to stay with me. You can go to my house now, have a bath and go to sleep." He ordered a young policeman to take the boy to his house and stay with him. Then his duties and responsibilities overwhelmed him again.

Late that afternoon, a wealthy man named Tsukigawa, whom Mr. Toyoshima knew vaguely, paid him a visit. "Sir, my young nephew lived somewhere around here. I have been told that his mother, brother and sister have all been killed. Only he still survives. Do you have any idea where he is?"

When he described the missing nephew, Mr. Toyoshima recounted the story of the dying family. "I think this must surely be your nephew. He is now at my house. I know he will be happy to see you." He gave the man directions to his house and watched him bow gratefully out of the office. Well, the boy has a family again, he thought, and was glad.

But within an hour, Mr. Tsukigawa was back, looking anxious. "I went to your house, sir, and searched everywhere. But the boy is not there."

"What?" Mr. Toyoshima stood up, alarmed. "That can't be. I know he was taken there. Wait here. I'll see what happened."

Minutes later, he knew the whole story. The young policeman had indeed taken the boy to his home, seen to his bath and fixed him a meal. Then, suddenly, the boy had grown extremely weak and begun bleeding from the mouth, so he had quickly taken him to the Shinoyozen Primary School aid center. The medical people there had promised to care for the boy, and the policeman had returned to duty.

With this new information, the two men went to the rescue center, several blocks away. No, they were told, there was no record of such a 6-year-old boy being admitted. But there are so many, you must understand.

Mr. Toyoshima was unable to accept defeat. This boy had been his personal responsibility. So he, along with the anxious uncle, began to circulate among the patients there, asking questions. A boy? About six? Pale and weak? Bleeding from the mouth? No, we didn't see him. Then, there was one who remembered, who had seen a boy. It was an old man. There were bandages across his upper body, but his eyes were still bright.

"A young boy about six?" he said thoughtfully. "I remember one such boy brought here about noon. He was in bad shape. I think he died a few hours later, though I can't be sure."

So that was it, thought Mr. Toyoshima. That was why they had not found a trace. He had been here so briefly that his entry had never even been registered on the record. The body of the little boy must have been cremated by the time they got there.

The old patient held up something in his hand. "The little boy gave me this," he whispered. "He told me that it was a present, a present for . . . me."

The old man's hand was steady, and Mr. Toyoshima could see quite clearly what it held. It clutched a chipped, wooden doll.

Ray Gallagher, aboard *Bock's Car,* was holding a different kind of doll—a blonde, blue-eyed doll named Mary Ann which his little niece had given him as a Christmas present in 1944. Ray was more convinced than ever that the doll was his good-luck charm, for it had brought him safely through this last mission, the most hair-raising he had ever flown.

Ray, aged 23, had played baseball for the Chicago White Sox before entering service in 1942. At first, he had talked a lot about returning to baseball, but lately, he seemed to have changed his mind. He began talking about getting married (he was engaged) and starting a business, "any kind of business just so long as I'm my own boss." As a matter of fact, he was thinking about his girl on the trip back, and the blonde doll never left his hands.

The plane had taken off from Okinawa at about 1530 hours, destination: Tinian. Sweeney and Ashworth had sent a confirming strike message from Okinawa to General Farrell on Tinian, and once airborne all the crew had to do was relax for the seven-hour flight. As the plane flew through the gathering darkness, there was little jubilation on board, no mood of celebration. They had done their job, but there was no gloating over it. The crew, for the most part, was silent, each man withdrawn into himself. Many hoped that what they had accomplished would send them home at last.

For Bombardier Kermit Beahan, 26, home was Houston, Texas, where he had graduated from Rice University. Handsome, about six feet tall and 220 pounds, "Honey Bee" was an athlete, a ladies' man, a crack bombardier, and one of the most popular men in the entire 393rd Squadron. He had flown in the European, African and Pacific theaters, and even before the Nagasaki mission had earned his first (of three) Distinguished Flying Crosses. He had been shot down four times, but he had escaped without injury. "You can't hurt me," he used to say. "I played football in Texas, and after a few games with those Texas boys, there's nothing can hurt you."

For Copilot Charles Donald Albury, nicknamed "Donald Duck" for his stoutness and slightly waddling walk, home was Miami, Florida, where his wife and 10-month-old daughter awaited his safe return. Like Sweeney, Don had decided young on a flying career. He had taken his first flying lessons at 18. He had attended Miami University and joined the air-cadet program in 1942. An exceptionally able pilot, he had been a flight instructor and was the aircraft commander when Sweeney, as squadron commander, did not fly a mission.

During the trip back, Albury, a deeply religious man, prayed to God that what they had just done would help end the fighting and killing.

At one point, Sweeney looked over his shoulder and saw that several of the men had fallen asleep. He was glad. They had earned it. Then he noticed that Fred Olivi was wide awake, his eyes fixed straight ahead, unwavering. "Everything OK, Fred?" he asked.

Olivi shook his head, as if coming awake. "Wh-what? Oh. Yeah, Major. Everything's OK." Olivi was the one member of the crew who had not been on the Hiroshima mission, so for him, the atomic bomb exploding over Nagasaki was new and frightening. Yet he still believed that they had done the only thing possible. It would save many lives in the long run.

Olivi, a second-generation Italian-American from Chicago and a devout Catholic, was five feet seven inches tall and weighed a hefty 195 pounds. He was forever repeating a joke other crews in the squadron had coined, to the effect that the reason his plane always flew with its nose lower than its tail was that the officers up front—Sweeney, Albury, Beahan and himself—were so much heavier than the poor enlisted men in the rear. Though a dedicated trencherman, Olivi neither drank nor smoked. He had always worried about his age, 22, and how young he must have appeared to the others. Today had changed that. He figured that he had grown up rather suddenly.

Sergeant Edward K. Buckley, 33, from Lisbon, Ohio, was asleep and dreaming of dogs, lean, gray dogs going round and round an oval track. Buckley, who had attended veterinary school, was a passionate dog-racing buff and he would talk all day about "the hounds" if given half a chance. Called "Muscles" by his fellow NCOs because of his thin and spindly build, Buck was a great joke-teller and an even greater beer-drinker. He had always wanted to go to Iwo Jima where, he had heard, they had unrationed beer. He said his greatest disappointment in the Army was finally getting to Iwo and finding *no* beer on the entire island. Now he smiled in his sleep. He had just backed a winner.

About three hours from Tinian, *Bock's Car* encountered

turbulence. Pappy Dehart had been asleep in his turret, but the sudden dip of the plane jolted him awake. He didn't know where he was for a minute. Then he remembered and he sat staring out at the blackness beyond his bubble window. There is no one quite so lonely in a B-29 as the tail-gunner. He has to be somewhat of a "loner" to endure the isolation, and Albert (Pappy) Dehart was.

Dehart was from Plainview, Texas. At 35, he was the father of three children. A quiet, unassuming man, he was one of the best tail-gunners in the business. He didn't seem to mind his isolated position. "If I have to be in the Army, I'm just as glad to be a tail-gunner," he once said. "It gives me time to think, and I've got a lot on my mind." What he had on his mind at that moment was the image of a giant mushroom cloud getting closer and closer.

The tossing airplane had also awakened Navigator James F. Van Pelt, and as he sat hunched over his navigation charts he began thinking of babies. For Van Pelt, 27, the war had interrupted his plans to become a doctor. He hailed from Oak Hill, West Virginia, and had taken pe-med training at Virginia Polytechnic Institute. Quiet, studious, soft-spoken, Van Pelt had earned the respect of both officers and enlisted men for his competence and consideration. Now, riding in the darkness, Van Pelt wondered whether all the babies he would ever deliver would equal the lives just lost.

One person who was very glad this particular mission was nearly over was Master Sergeant John D. Kuharek. Fuel consumption had been his responsibility, and this time he had almost failed in his duty. Kuharek, 32, was regular Army, a tough, professional soldier. He had been in training to be a priest until the age of 18 when he had given up the idea and enlisted in the U. S. Army. That had been in 1931, in the heart of the Great Depression, and the Army—"see the world, find adventure in uniform"—had a certain appeal for a poor boy from Pittsburgh. Kuharek figured that on this particular day he had found just about enough adventure to last a lifetime.

Chuck Sweeney relaxed his hold on the wheel. They had passed through the turbulence, and he sat back, remembering the many moments of this unforgettable flight—the trapped fuel, the fouled-up rendezvous, the frustrating abort at Kokura, the near-fiasco over Nagasaki, the lost radio and the hairy landing at Okinawa. But the event that stuck in his mind was the interview with General James Doolittle. When Sweeney had reported to the general, head of 8th Air Force on Okinawa, on landing there, General Doolittle, ramrod-straight and unsmiling, had received the news of the Nagasaki atomic-bomb strike with no display of emotion. To Sweeney, an impulsive and volatile Irishman, it seemed almost unnatural. He had looked forward to this meeting—between Doolittle, the man who had ignited the whole air campaign against Japan with his epic Tokyo raid, and an unknown Air Force major who just possibly might have had a hand in finishing it, and all Doolittle could say was: "What was the extent of the damage, Major?"

"We can't be sure, General," Sweeney answered. "Smoke obscured everything."

"But target was hit?"

"Definitely, sir."

Doolittle was silent, staring down at his desk, perhaps remembering another mission three and a half years earlier. "It's been a long time coming, Sweeney," he finally murmured.

"Yes, sir. I hope it means the end."

Another long silence, and Sweeney, embarrassed, saluted and turned toward the door. Doolittle's voice, sharp, imperative, spun him around: "Sweeney!"

"Sir?"

"I can only tell you what they said to me." And the wrinkled face smiled that famous wintry smile. "Well done!"

Now Sweeney could also smile at the memory. It meant something—a "well done" from Jimmy Doolittle. He sighed. They were almost home.

CHAPTER 16

The Long Day, the Long Night

FOR SOME PEOPLE AUGUST 9 SEEMED NEVER TO END, AS THE long, pain-filled hours stretched through the night. One was 45-year-old Sadayoshi Nagao.

The day started ordinarily when he reported for work at eight o'clock at the Mitsubishi Arms Factory. He was on time as always, for he believed that he, as foreman of his department, should set an example of reliability for the others. That morning, the air-raid alarm had sounded earlier than was customary. All the workers in his department had moved to the air-raid shelters, but without any great sense of urgency, and had returned to their jobs a half hour later. The planes had passed harmlessly over Nagasaki on their way to bomb the air base at Omura, twenty-six miles to the north.

Engrossed in his work, Mr. Nagao first realized that something violent had happened outside the building when he looked out the window and saw a telephone pole tilting crazily. Then, fused in several seconds, came the great wind, the heat, the noise and the sound of someone yelling: "We've been hit. They got the factory dead-center." At that point Mr. Nagao lost consciousness.

Hours later he revived, and discovered that the lower part of his body was pinned beneath the wreckage of the room. Although he felt no pain, he could not move his legs. Gradually he cleared away some of the debris trapping him and slithered out from under the rest. Once free, he stood up and slowly tried to make sense out of the remains of the room. Three of the four walls were gone as was most of the ceiling; the place was partially filled with a thin, black smoke, and he could hear the crackling of flames coming from somewhere. To his right, he saw two men half-covered by the wreckage. He squatted and tried to push away the debris. It was then that he saw their blood and felt their stillness. He slid his hand beneath one man's shirt. There was no heartbeat. He stared slowly around the room, now aware that there might well be other bodies buried here. What calamity had engulfed him?

He staggered away from the dead man and out into the yard. Now his feet felt light and he ran easily from the hateful place, oblivious of the stares of the people he passed in the streets, oblivious even of the people themselves. It was only when his head began to pound that he stopped. Through a haze, he saw a dugout nearby. A number of bodies lay in front of it, their arms outstretched as if reaching for some unattainable goal. Inside, it was even worse—hot and crowded with people who were moaning or crying for water. But it was relatively dark and anonymous and Mr. Nagao was greatful to find a hole he could crawl into.

He sank wearily to the mud floor, his back resting against a sandbag. His head ached fiercely and when he looked down he saw blood on his shirt where it must have dripped from a gash somewhere on his head. His fingers tenderly located the wound on the side of his head; it had already clotted over and dried.

After a while, several women entered the dugout carrying water, and when they set down the buckets the people in the dugout scrambled to get at them, clawing at each other, pushing, grabbing. A young man crawling across Mr. Nagao's legs stopped suddenly and looked at him. "Would you like some water, sir?" he asked. His face was red and his shirt had been blown off, exposing his thin ribs. "That's very kind of you," Mr. Nagao answered. "But, please, first get some for yourself." The boy nodded and resumed his slow crawling. Minutes later he was back, carrying a teacup full of water. Mr. Nagao drank it gratefully. He wished there were more.

The odor in the dugout—a combination of burnt flesh, sweat, blood and the smell of fear—was distinctive now, and Mr. Nagao was just beginning to wonder if medical care would soon be forthcoming when four or five young women from the Rescue Corps came into the dugout. They began examining each person, and, whenever it was indicated, they would bandage wounds or pass out medicine. All too quickly, however, the medicine was gone, and the people who had not been treated either sank back, too exhausted and dispirited to protest, or began to complain loudly.

From his spot in the corner of the long shelter, Mr. Nagao watched it all and felt a disgust rise in him when he observed that those people who seemed to be the least injured were the ones who cried the loudest for help. When a man is wounded and in pain, he thought, he seems to lose any ability to be objective. All that he cares about is the easing of his own pain, and the devil with the other fellow!

With the medicine exhausted, the young corpswomen did not seem to know what to do next. Mr. Nagao tried to stand up, but his feet felt as if they were on fire. They were very swollen and red now, so he gave up the idea of walking. Instead, he started crawling over to where the oldest-looking of the young women was standing. "Miss," he called, "perhaps these people would feel better if they could get something to eat. Are there any melons or eggplants around outside?" The girl nodded and she and two others quickly went out. Mr. Nagao crawled back to his spot and sank back again. He himself had no appetite whatsoever, but he reasoned that something solid might just cheer the others up a bit.

A few minutes later, the young women brought in handfuls of eggplants and melons, carried them to Mr. Nagao and dumped them all in front of him. The girl to whom he had spoken asked: "Would you, sir, please pass these out to the other people?" He nodded and set to work tearing the tender eggplants and melons into large pieces which were then quickly passed from hand to hand until they were gone. He looked around and saw that some of the people were devouring the food hungrily, while others, still dazed by pain or shock, simply sat holding the pieces in their hands, staring listlessly at them.

It was growing dark now and through the dugout opening Mr. Nagao could see the flickering firelight from the burning city. The girls from the Rescue Corps were moving among the people trying to write down their names and addresses. When they reached Mr. Nagao he told them who he was and where he came from. The young man, perhaps 17, who had crawled over his legs and had kindly brought him the cup of water, overheard him, and said that he was from the same town. The boy's father was actually an acquaintance of Mr. Nagao.

As the darkness deepened, the bad smell increased. It was inevitable, thought Mr. Nagao, for now he was aware that for hours people had been quietly dying one by one; he could tell by the sudden silence coming from a spot where there had been cries and moaning. Just a few minutes ago, he had personally brushed hands with death. A young man, lying next to him, had told Mr. Nagao in a very weak voice that he had been in the Nagasaki Medical College when the bomb exploded. He had been recounting its terrible effect on the buildings when his voice trailed off, and Mr. Nagao had reached out a hand and touched his arm. But he quickly pulled back his hand. The arm was already cold and lifeless.

With the cries diminishing, a muffled silence descended, punctuated by an occasional moan or sob. Suddenly a woman stood up and shouted: "Let me out! I must go to the toilet! Let me out!" Hurriedly, she pushed her way between the bodies and out of the dugout. Minutes passed, but she did not come back. Mr. Nagao felt unaccountably saddened by her disappearance. It was as if she had deserted the entire group by leaving the dugout. She never did return.

It began to get cold, and Mr. Nagao started to move closer to the warmth of his neighbor until he remembered that his neighbor was dead. He shivered and tried to pull his shirt up around his neck. It was then that he felt a tickling on his arms and neck. When he felt with exploratory fingers, he realized that the ants had discovered them. Somehow this depressed him even more. They were only fit for the ants now, he thought.

It must have been close to midnight when the Rescue Corps women returned to the dugout and informed them that those who could make it should now go to the railroad station where they would be transported to the medical barracks in Omura. So the exodus started, people hobbling on improvised crutches, women leaning on men or on other women, others crawling slowly—all who could muster any strength of purpose left the dugout. Most of those who remained would remain permanently.

Mr. Nagao had decided to stay where he was. For one thing, his feet were so swollen and sore by this time that it was pure agony to put any weight on them. Also, he didn't see much point in leaving in the middle of the night, to exchange a reasonably comfortable shelter (if one could ignore the smell) for a less secure and colder waiting area, probably out in the open. He would wait until morning before making any move.

He looked around, squinting into the darkness. There was still enough firelight coming in through the dugout opening for him to make out a few still forms on the ground. Not very pleasant surroundings, he thought, and for a second he wondered if his decision to stay had been wise after all. Suddenly he was startled to hear a soft voice saying: "It is Mr. Nagao, is it not?" He turned and saw that it was the boy with whom he had been talking earlier.

"Yes," he answered. "I see that you decided to stay here too."

There was a pause, then the boy said, "It seemed more sensible to wait until morning."

"Quite right. Exactly." Mr. Nagao felt reassured by the words. "How are you feeling?"

"Oh, I'm all right. Just a little tired. How is your head?"

"It hurts some, but the bleeding has stopped."

"I'm glad of that." Again the young man paused, then asked, "Do you think our families are safe?"

"I'm sure of it," Mr. Nagao said quickly. "After all, they are more than fifteen miles from here. I don't see how one bomb, however powerful it was, could have done them any harm."

He heard the boy moving restlessly, then a sudden sharp gasp as if he were in pain.

"Are you sure you are all right?" he asked anxiously.

"Y-yes," the boy answered hesitantly. "It . . . it was just a sharp rock."

Mr. Nagao listened to the boy's quickly-drawn breaths. Gradually, they slowed to normal, but the boy was silent for quite a long time and he began to be concerned. Then the boy asked, "Do you think there is any water around, Mr. Nagao?"

"I don't think so. But I could crawl outside and look."

"Oh, no. It's not important." He sighed deeply. "What time do you think it is?"

"It must be about one in the morning."

"One in the morning," the boy echoed. "Four more hours until dawn."

"Why don't you try to get some sleep?" Mr. Nagao suggested.

"I tried to, but the . . . smell . . ."

"Yes. It's pretty bad, I know. But you should try."

"All right. I will try again."

And apparently the boy was able to sleep, for he remained quiet. Mr. Nagao himself dozed fitfully. Once he woke up and turned over and the boy spoke softly to him. "Are you awake now, Mr. Nagao?"

"Yes. Couldn't you sleep?"

"Not very much. How are you feeling?" The boy's voice sounded much weaker.

"Better, thank you. And you?"

"I'm all right. You know, I'm glad you're awake because I wanted to tell you how happy I am that you are here in the dugout with me. I have been thinking of my mother and father and my little brother and I was missing them so much. Then you woke up and when I heard your voice I knew I wasn't alone anymore."

Mr. Nagao was a little embarrassed and he quickly changed the subject. "Tell me, what are you going to be when you grow up?"

"I . . . I was going to be a doctor," the boy said slowly. Then suddenly he sat up straight and pointed to the dugout opening. "Look!" he cried. "The light has come. Dawn is nearly here."

Half an hour later, the two went outside. They sat on the ground, gratefully breathing the cool, fresh air. Out now in the light, Mr. Nagao was aghast to see how badly injured the boy was. The entire right side of his face and neck looked as if that part of him had been resting on a glowing hibachi all night long, so burnt and black it was. He must have been in great pain throughout the night, but he had said nothing, had never complained.

He watched the boy rise and walk slowly to a pile of debris. He poked into it with his foot, then reached down and extracted a thin piece of wood about three feet long. He brought it back to Mr. Nagao and, tucking it under his arm, he held out both hands. "Let me help you to your feet, sir."

Mr. Nagao struggled to his feet, wincing at the pain. The boy handed him the stick and he leaned on it. It did help a little. How kind the young man was—to think of him, Mr. Nagao, when he himself was obviously so much more seriously wounded. "Thank you," he murmured.

"I think we should try to find a medical-aid station," the boy said.

"Yes. Your . . . your face needs treatment, I think."

The boy said nothing, simply took Mr. Nagao by the other arm and helped him along. They did not talk, for each was preoccupied, looking at the strange and terrible world around them. Mr. Nagao was astonished at the completeness of the devastation.

Finally, they reached the factory and it was almost unrecognizable, with only a few steel girders still pointing skyward. At one of the gates was a medical-aid station and they headed in that direction, but suddenly the boy stumbled and fell. "I can't go on any longer, Mr. Nagao," he said weakly. "I'm sorry."

A nurse hurried over, took one look at the boy, then disappeared again. The boy looked imploringly at Mr. Nagao. "Water," he whispered. "Could I please have some water?"

Mr. Nagao saw a bucket of water on the ground nearby with a cracked cup beside it. He filled the cup and carried it back to the boy. The boy's eyes were closed. Mr. Nagao leaned down and gently raised his head. Some of the water entered the boy's mouth, but most trickled down his chin. "Thank you, Mr. Nagao," the boy said softly. "Please tell

. . . my parents that I was . . . with a friend . . . at the end."

Suddenly, the boy opened his eyes and looked up into Mr. Nagao's face. "Why?" he whispered, his eyes wide and innocent. "Why?" Then his eyes closed once more, he shuddered and went limp.

Mr. Nagao lowered the boy's head to the ground and stood up, his knees trembling. He knew that the boy was dead, yet he found it hard to accept. They had spent only a few hours together, but those hours had drawn them close to each other. For they had shared the same bomb and the same dark, stinking dugout. Now they would no longer share anything.

For many minutes, Mr. Nagao stood looking at the boy lying in front of him. Incredibly, there was a hint of a smile on the ravaged young face, and Mr. Nagao suddenly remembered his thoughts a few hours earlier when he had been mentally condemning the self-pitying actions of those people in the dugout. Now he realized that he had been wrong. The boy had shown him how wrong he had been. He had proved that certain people, even in the most terrible circumstances, can retain a measure of dignity.

At last, Mr. Nagao turned and, his swollen feet ignored, walked slowly away from the still figure on the ground. He had discovered something that he should never have forgotten: Man's indomitable courage.

CHAPTER 17

End of the Mission

2230 HOURS

Bock's Car LANDED IN THE DARKNESS OF TINIAN AT 10:30 THAT night. The men were silent, exhausted. They had been flying Special Mission No. 16 for some twenty hours. Physically, emotionally, they were drained—and glad of only one thing: They were home. It was over.

When the plane taxied up to the hardstand, there were no klieg lights, no photographers, no medal-awarding ceremonies. Chuck Sweeney, peering through the window, saw only a few ground-crew personnel, no one else. Maybe they've forgotten all about us, he thought wryly. Then he caught sight of two motionless figures standing just off the hardstand. One of them looked like Colonel Tibbets.

The crew gathered their gear and slowly climbed out. Sweeney was the last to leave the aircraft. Just before he lowered himself through the hole, he glanced back to where the Bomb had sat. Now there was just an empty black shadow.

The two waiting men came up to him. Along with Tibbets

was Admiral Parnel, looking pale and worried. Sweeney himself was too tired even to salute. The other two officers seemed not to notice.

Said Tibbets softly, "Pretty rough, Chuck?"

"Pretty rough, Colonel."

The two men looked at each other. No further words were needed. They had both been in the same pit. They were unique—the only two men who had ever dropped It.

Admiral Parnel cleared his throat. "You know, Major, those hours just before you dropped the bomb, we'd just about given up on you." Both he and General Farrell had been desperately worried when no news of the drop had been received. When they were at lunch, a messenger had rushed in with a dispatch from Major Hopkins in the third plane, which had never made contact with the others. Hopkins, confused and almost certain by then that the mission had failed, had broken radio silence to inquire: "Has Sweeney aborted?"

But somehow, the first word was lost in transmission, and the message that was placed in General Farrell's nervous hands only confirmed his worst suspicions. Without preamble, General Thomas F. Farrell abruptly lost his lunch.

". . . although we were worried," Parnel was saying now, "Tibbets here said if anyone could get it done, you could. I see he was right."

"It was close," Sweeney admitted, then grinned. "What the hell are we so gloomy about? Mission was accomplished. Now what about some beer?"

Tibbets looked a little sheepish. "I'm afraid the beer ran out, Chuck. But maybe the medics have some medicinal whiskey left."

"What the hell are we waiting for?"

But first came the debriefing where each man told in detail what he remembered about the mission. Then everyone turned in their flight logs, and the entire crew—officers and enlisted men alike—headed for the officers' quarters. Usually, they had to go to the medical detachment for the "medicinal" stimulants. But this time the pretense had been abandoned, and a bar had been set up with real bourbon and Scotch whiskey at the officers club. The men, after being up two days and two nights, proceeded to drink with a dogged determination, until one by one, their voices slurred, their eyelids drooped, and their memories dimmed, they staggered off to bed and sleep.

By 5:00 A.M., only two men were left, Tom Ferebee, navigator of the *Enola Gay,* who had joined the party, and his best friend, Jimmy Van Pelt, who had just navigated this mission. At that hour the whiskey had run out, and Van Pelt and Ferebee had stumbled out into the morning air. Before them was General Farrell's jeep. They grinned at each other, hopped in, and began driving wildly around the area, hollering and laughing.

The jeep stopped only when the two men tried to drive it straight through the Quonset hut where Albury and Beahan were sleeping. It was Beahan who stood up in the shambles, clad only in his skin and his debonair moustache, and shouted, "Hey, do you guys know what yesterday was?"

There was a sudden silence, as Van Pelt looked sharply at Beahan. But he realized immediately that the bombardier must be referring to something else, to something other than what had first popped into his mind.

"No, Bea," he said. "What day was it?"

"It was my birthday, that's what it was," he yelled. "It was my goddamned birthday!"

Four hundred yards away, General Farrell slept through the commotion, unaware that his jeep had just been wrecked. A few hours earlier, he had sent a top-secret cable to the commanding general, 20th AAF, with the heading "Centerboard." It had stated:

Strike and accompanying airplanes have returned to Tinian. Ashworth message No. 44 from Okinawa is confirmed by all observers. Cloud cover was bad at strike and strike plane had barely enough fuel to reach Okinawa. After listening to the accounts, one gets the impression of a supremely tough job carried out with determination, sound judgment and great skill. It is fortunate for the success of the mission that its leaders, Sweeney and Ashworth, were men of stamina and stout heart. Weaker men could not have done this job. Ashworth feels confident that the bomb was satisfactorily placed and that it did its job well.

Just how well was even then being determined in a bomb shelter in the heart of the Japanese Empire.

2345 HOURS

THOUGH HE ONLY HALF-SUSPECTED THAT IT WOULD HAPPEN, Mr. Hisatsune Sakomizu, Chief Secretary of the Suzuki Cabinet, was about to participate in one of history's epic dramas. Mr. Sakomizu did not know of General Farrell's top-secret cable from Tinian, but if he had, he probably would have thought that there was a certain inevitability to it. Up until now, the ruling powers of Japan had been unable to reach any decision about the future course of the war. And so, an Imperial Conference had been convened a half hour ago on this August 9th night. All that was needed now was the presence of Emperor Hirohito.

Secretary Sakomizu sat in the hot, airless shelter-room where the conference would take place and saw the door behind the throne open and the Emperor emerge. The moment had come. Because Sakomizu was "in" on the secret, he knew that this was the climactic moment of the long affair.

For Secretary Sakomizu, the last three days had been a series of undisguised shocks. The first had been a brief report from 2nd Army headquarters on the Hiroshima raid and the new, enormously destructive type of bomb used there. Then, at three in the morning on August 7, he had been awakened by a telephone call from Mr. Saiji Hasegawa, chief of the foreign news desk of the Domei News Bureau.

"Mr. Sakomizu, have you heard the news from the United States?" the newsman asked excitedly.

"What news?"

"I have just monitored a radio broadcast from San Francisco and heard the American President speaking."

"President Truman?" Sakomizu asked incredulously. "What did he say?"

"He said that the United States had been able to produce an atomic bomb and that it had just been dropped on Hiroshima."

Mr. Sakomizu took a deep breath. An atomic bomb! "Yes," he said matter-of-factly, "we suspected as much when we first heard of it. Would you please send me the full text of the speech as soon as it has been translated?"

"Yes, sir, of course. But what should we print about this news?"

"You will be advised shortly." He hung up.

He had tried to sound calm, to reflect an assurance that he did not feel. Actually, he was astonished. An atomic bomb! Japan herself had conducted extensive research on atomic energy, and six months earlier, at a conference of the country's leading physicists, it had been the unanimous conclusion that from an industrial point of view no nation could possibly make an atomic bomb for at least three or four more years. How had the United States done it?

His question was answered a few hours later when the full text of President Truman's speech was delivered to him. In it the President explained how hard scientists in the United States had worked and how huge had been the amount of money spent in the undertaking. He went on to point out that now that a weapon of such tremendous force had finally been made, there was only one course of action for Japan to take: Immediate acceptance of the Potsdam Declaration and unconditional surrender.

As the day progressed, it became clear that the Hiroshima bombing was indeed a serious threat to Japan's leaders. But the first reaction was outrage. At the Cabinet meeting on Tuesday, Foreign Minister Togo proposed that the Japanese Government file a strong protest through the Swiss Embassy in Tokyo and the League of Red Cross Societies against the dropping of such a bomb and demand the immediate cessation of its use, just as poisonous gas had been outlawed. Cabinet approval had been given to his proposal.

Some of the Cabinet ministers thought that now that the atomic bomb had been used against the people, Japan should quickly end the war and accept the Potsdam Declaration. The main opposition to this suggestion came from the military leaders, particularly War Minister Anami who declared that it was foolish to assume that it even was an atomic bomb; it might well be just a trick by the enemy. An on-the-spot investigation should be made to evaluate the bomb's power before any decision was taken. Consequently, the Cabinet dispatched Dr. Yoshio Nishina, Japan's nuclear expert, to the scene of the bombing. It was also decided to refer to the Hiroshima bomb in the newspapers as a "new-type" bomb, instead of using the word atomic. General Anami was insistent on one point: The idea of surrender was premature. The prestige of the military would never entertain such a proposal.

The aged and respected Premier Suzuki quickly tried to puncture this argument. "Now that the atomic bomb has appeared," he said, "the war must be ended. This is not a defeat of the Japanese armed forces at the hands of U. S. forces, but rather the defeat of Japanese science and technology by U. S. technology. Therefore, the military should not speak of prestige."

But the military leaders remained unconvinced, and nothing had been settled. All through August 7 and 8, the secretary's office had been full of visitors, wanting to see the premier, hoping to sway him toward one side or the other. Sakomizu found himself in agreement with Premier Suzuki's point of view—that further defense of the homeland was futile in the face of the powerful new weapon.

Dr. Nishina's report on Hiroshima was made on the evening of August 8. He came directly to the secretary's room and said in a tremulous voice: "It can only have been an atomic bomb to cause such havoc. We scientists must apologize to the nation for our incompetence." Then, stunned by what he had seen at Hiroshima and saddened by what he believed to be his failure as a scientist, he had broken down completely.

Secretary Sakomizu had immediately relayed Nishina's information to Premier Suzuki, who then instructed him to "prepare for a council meeting tomorrow to discuss matters pertaining to the termination of the war, as I believe that time has come at last. The Emperor, I hope, will attend." Then Suzuki had hurried off to confer with the Emperor.

But before that meeting could be convened, the second great blow had fallen. At about 3:00 A.M., on the ninth, Mr. Sakomizu was again wakened by a ringing telephone. Picking it up, he heard the familiar voice of news chief Hasegawa.

"Once more, I am the bearer of bad news, Mr. Secretary," he said apologetically.

"What is it this time?"

"The Soviet Union just declared war on us."

Astounded, the secretary could only murmur, "Is it true? Is it really true?"

"I'm afraid so. I'll let you know the details as soon as they come in. I'm sorry."

Secretary Sakomizu replaced the phone slowly, unable to comprehend the news. Then, suddenly, came anger. At the very moment when a Japanese ambassador was in Moscow trying to get the Soviets to act as intermediaries in a peace feeler, that country had attacked Japan. It was like asking for bread and getting a stone thrown in return. The secretary would have been surprised to know that his feelings at that moment were very similar to those of millions of Americans on a Sunday afternoon in December four years earlier.

The Emperor would attend a conference that evening, Mr. Sakomizu learned when he arrived at his office. Meanwhile, the premier said, every effort should be made to reach an agreement before that meeting. As a result, at 11:00 A.M., just as Chuck Sweeney's plane was approaching Nagasaki, a conference of the Supreme War Council was getting under way at the Imperial Palace. Again, no agreement was reached on what should be done, despite the new information received. For it was in the middle of this meeting that the third blow fell. A military aide entered bearing the news of the second atomic bomb just dropped on the city of Nagasaki. It was a crushing setback for those military leaders who had convinced themselves and others that the United States had had only one bomb, that in destroying Hiroshima, the Americans had "shot their wad." They had argued that Hiroshima could now be turned into an advantage, a rallying point for millions of Japanese to "Remember Hiroshima! Defend Your Country! Death to the Invader!" But Nagasaki had changed all that. It had demonstrated that the rain of death would continue, as the Allies had warned. Hiroshima was no one-shot, do-or-die gamble. Nagasaki had been leveled a mere three days later. Other cities presumably would follow. The military men could no longer shy away from the truth. If Hiroshima had been the coffin, Nagasaki had been the lid and the nails that sealed it.

But the die-hard militarists could still not swallow the bitter pill of unconditional surrender. How could they be reconciled to the inevitable? Early in the afternoon Premier Suzuki announced a council meeting for 11:30 that night, adding casually that the Emperor would be present. There was surprise, but no objection. The Emperor never took part in such a discussion, merely gave his blessing to whatever decision the council reached.

That night, at 11:30, a full-dress Imperial Conference met to decide the fate of Japan. On hand were eleven men, the six ruling members of government, four secretaries and aides, and one guest, Baron Hiranuma, president of the privy council which advised the Emperor. The Big Six were split into two main groups which could loosely be labeled the "war faction" and the "peace faction." The war group consisted of War Minister Korechika Anami, a stubborn, moustached 57-year-old general, Chief of Staff Umezo, a gruff, fanatical martinet, and Navy Chief of Staff Soemu Toyodo, an eloquent and impassioned speaker. Ranged against Anami, Umezo and Toyodo were the 81-year-old Premier, Kantaro Suzuki, an expert at treading the dangerous area between extremists in wartime Japan, Foreign Minister Togo, who would later be branded a war criminal by the Allies for his part in Pearl Harbor, and Admiral Yonai, a 65-year-old advocate of peace. The eighteen-by-thirty-foot room in the air-raid shelter was not air-conditioned and within minutes in the sultry August heat, all those present were sweltering in their formal clothes.

Shortly before midnight, the door behind the throne opened and Emperor Hirohito entered, accompanied by his aide-de-camp. Mr. Sakomizu was dismayed by his Emperor's appearance. He looked completely exhausted, his right cheek was jumping with a nervous tic, and several strands of hair hung limply over his forehead. Everyone present bowed and the Emperor, sighing heavily, sat down. He was unutterably depressed by the recent chain of events. In 1926, when he had become the 124th Emperor of Japan, he had hopefully chosen the name *Showa* to signify his reign. It meant Peace. Now, as he looked around at the shambles of what had been the glorious Japanese Empire, he realized what a mockery that term had become.

On a cloth-covered table in front of the Emperor were three documents: A translation of the Potsdam Declaration, and two papers marked Plan A and Plan B. Plan A was an acceptance of the Allied proclamation with the sole condition that the Emperor system be retained in Japan; Plan B stipulated three other conditions as well, such as the handling of war criminals, disarmament of troops, and nonoccupation of the home islands. In earlier meetings, there had been an equal split between the two plans.

To open the conference, Premier Suzuki asked Secretary Sakomizu to read the Potsdam Declaration, which he did nervously under the gaze of the Emperor. When Sakomizu finished stating the terms which everyone in the room knew full well, Suzuki asked Foreign Minister Togo for his opinion. The 63-year-old diplomat, a bespectacled, aloof man, rose slowly and bowed to the Emperor. He outlined recent developments in a calm voice, then concluded: "It is a distasteful thing to do, but what other choice have we? We must accept the Potsdam Declaration with, of course, the Plan A proviso. To attach any other conditions would be tantamount to rejecting the Allies' offer. They would only regard such an action as a challenge. What choice do we have?" He bowed reverently and sat down.

Premier Suzuki turned quickly to Admiral Yonai and asked for his views on the subject. The navy minister had been an outspoken critic of the war against the United States in the first place and had been virtually exiled for over three years. But his close friend Suzuki had called him back into government. Now, without bothering to rise, he said stiffly: "I agree completely with Foreign Minister Togo."

Suzuki nodded, pleased with the answer, and turned to War Minister Anami, the focal point of the opposition. "General Anami?" he asked. "What is your opinion?"

At that juncture, General Anami had one small hope left: To make the Americans suffer so grievously in any invasion of the homeland that they would be willing to compromise at the peace table. Only in that way could some honor and "face" be salvaged for the military. One last great battle, that was his theme and he meant to stick to it.

Now he said firmly: "I am opposed to the views of the foreign minister. We can still win a decisive battle on the homeland. We must fight—to the death if necessary. I believe that our people would find great satisfaction in dying with such honor."

When Suzuki asked him if he could find it possible to support Plan A if the others so voted, General Anami shook his head and his lips tightened in grim lines. "Never," he whispered. "And only in the last extreme could I accept Plan B."

The next speakers followed predictable patterns. Baron Hiranuma, after some searching questions about the military preparedness of the country, followed Togo's lead, although he had no vote. The other two "war faction" supporters, Admiral Toyodo and General Umezo, echoed Anami's line of thinking. The impasse remained unbroken—three against two; Suzuki had not yet cast his vote. The arguments went on.

Finally, two hours later, Premier Suzuki stood up and as Secretary Sakomizu studied his face he felt sure that the time had come. He knew Suzuki had anticipated the impasse and conferred secretly with the Emperor about it. The others fell silent, fully expecting the premier to express his own views on the subject and cast his vote. Instead, he said in a soft voice: "Gentlemen, we have spent hours in deliberation without coming to a decision and agreement is not yet in sight. You are fully aware that we cannot afford to waste even a moment at this juncture. I propose, therefore, to seek the Imperial guidance and substitute it for the decision of this conference." Premier Suzuki then turned, walked slowly to the throne, and bowed to Emperor Hirohito.

His words electrified the group. Everyone present, with the exception of Sakomizu, gasped and stared at the tableau. To ask the Emperor to declare himself and actually *substitute his opinion for the decision of the conference* was so extraordinary that the council members to a man were thunderstruck. Such a possibility had never occurred to them, and by the time each man realized the implications behind such a move, it was too late to do anything.

Emperor Hirohito, a gentle man whose main interest was marine biology, stared straight ahead. He realized at this critical moment that he must speak as one voice for the millions of his subjects who could still be saved by what he said now. Before him, the aged Suzuki stood bowing and Hirohito murmured to him to return to his seat. The premier, deaf in one ear, apparently did not hear, for he cupped his hand about his ear. Then the Emperor stretched out his left hand pointing toward Suzuki's vacant seat, and the old man understood and moved back to it.

The Emperor leaned forward toward those awaiting his divine words. He spoke slowly, wanting to make his meaning perfectly clear.

"I agree with the foreign minister's proposal that we accept the Allied proclamation on the basis of the foreign minister's plan. The army and navy chiefs, arguing for one more decisive battle, state that they have a good chance against the enemy. But I cannot help but wonder at their logic. The other day, the army chief of staff reported to me on the defense measures being taken at Kujukuri Beach. Yet when my own aide-de-camp made a personal inspection, his report was very different. I also received a report that a certain division had been fully armed, yet my own sources of investigation revealed that the soldiers have not even been provided with bayonets or enough ammunition. In any great battle for our country under such conditions I fear for the very continuance of the Japanese race. In order to hand down the nation called Japan to posterity, there is no other way for me but to keep as many of its people alive so that they again may stand on their own feet."

His eyes filled with tears, his voice broken with grief, Hirohito spelled it out in terms that could not be misunderstood. "I cannot help feeling sad when I think of the people who have served me so faithfully, the soldiers and sailors who have been killed or wounded in far-off battles, the families who have lost all their worldly goods, and often their lives as well, in the air raids at home. I'm sure you realize that it is unbearable for me to see my brave soldiers suffer the dishonor of surrender. It is equally unbearable that others who have rendered only devoted service to me be punished as instigators of war. Nevertheless, the time has come when I—when all of us—must bear the unbearable."

The Emperor paused and when Secretary Sakomizu glanced furtively at him, he was heartsick to see his Emperor wipe the hollows of his eyes beneath his glasses with a white-gloved thumb. The Emperor was crying, like any other mortal being! The very thought of his sovereign's tears brought a wave of tears to his own eyes.

Then, in low tones, quite unexpected from his usual high-pitched voice, Emperor Hirohito concluded: "At this moment, all of you are apparently concerned about my future. But I must tell you and assure you that it is not important what becomes of me. I am unimportant. It is the people, my people, that matter. And that is the reason why I have made up my mind to bring the war to termination at once."

The moment Secretary Sakomizu heard those final words, his throat became constricted and he prostrated himself in total obeisance across his desk. Tears gushed from his eyes and splashed over the papers on his desk. No one in the room uttered a word. All were sobbing, for this meant the end of everything.

At last, Premier Suzuki arose and said in a shaking voice: "Emperor, we have understood your gracious wish."

With that, everyone stood up and bowed, and the Emperor left his seat and turned toward the door. He paused and made a gesture as if he were about to speak again. But he only nodded slightly to himself, and with heavy steps, withdrew from the room.

Once he had left, Premier Suzuki addressed the war council for the last time. "His Majesty's decision should be made the decision of this conference as well," he said gravely. No one disagreed, and the sound of sobbing filled the room. *Nippon wa menmoku wo ushinatta.* Japan had lost "face."

The Emperor's decision held firm, but not before the suicides of General Anami and many other top-ranking military leaders, and a determined but doomed palace revolt by a group of young military fanatics. Six days later, even as Japan wept and mourned over the only defeat she had ever suffered, America would go wild with joy. And with good reason. Pearl Harbor, Bataan, Corregidor, Bougainville, Iwo Jima, Tarawa, Okinawa—and thousands upon thousands of America's young men—had been avenged. The war was over.

CHAPTER 18

Nagasaki Hospital

2400 HOURS

IT WAS NEAR MIDNIGHT WHEN THE GENTLE DOCTOR, DR. SAKURAI, walked outside the gate of the Nagasaki First Branch Hospital and stood gazing at the city. Even then, blazing fires were reflected in the smoke in the skies, smoke that swirled and eddied in the currents of rising heat. The huge conflagration revealed the scorched earth on the hillsides and illuminated the ruins of the Chinzei Junior High School, the Urakami Cathedral, the Shiroyama and Yamazato primary schools. The Mitsubishi Steelworks was the brightest fire of all, burning with a steady glare, and he guessed that the piles of coal stored in the yards must have caught fire.

Dr. Sakurai tried to clear his mind, but memories of the last twelve hours kept intruding. First, his conversation with Mr. Tayama about the new-type bomb, then the explosion in the ward, the effort to get all the patients out of the hospital safely—Mr. Tsujimoto out in the pumpkin field, the people who had staggered up the hill only to die in the "Water of the Last Age," and his badly injured colleague, Dr. Miyazaki. But there was also Nurse Ozaki, always by his side.

There was one thought in particular that he tried to keep out of his mind, but at close to six o'clock Nurse Ozaki had asked him for the third or fourth time: "Have you heard anything about your mother?"

It was a question that Dr. Sakurai dreaded. Whenever a moment's pause allowed his thoughts to drift in that direction, he was so afraid of the answer that he plunged at once into mind-numbing work.

Still, he knew it had to be faced eventually. Though in good health, both his parents were aged and somewhat helpless. Since some people had not considered it safe to remain in the center of the city, he had found his parents a place near the hospital only two months earlier. His father, though retired, continued to go to work and prepare his legal briefs at the district court office every morning. But once he had gone, his mother was all by herself. What had happened to her on this terrible day?

Every now and then, since the explosion, he had paused to stare toward the southwest, and each time he was sure that he had seen flames coming from the house where his parents lived and where his mother had been alone. Could she possibly have been luckier than the others? He was obsessed by the condition of the men and women who had been working in their fields nearby, or who had been injured in the wreckage of their own houses. It seemed likely that his mother had fared no better than the others. Throughout the day, whenever he looked at seriously injured, or burned, older women, he felt a chill of apprehension. *She* might be the next one.

Nurse Ozaki suggested, in warm concern, that he take a few minutes off and try and find his mother. But he refused, saying, "If she is dead, the later she is found, the better it will be for me. At least I can keep busy now, and there is still so much to be done."

"If she is dead"—somehow he managed to put that ugly thought out of his mind, and continued to move among the afflicted, comforting and helping as best he could. He had just returned from tending to a group of people who had collapsed a mere hundred yards from the hospital, when his heart almost stopped at the two people he saw in front of him. Nurse Ozaki, with a radiant smile, was coming toward him leading his mother by the hand. She, too, was smiling at the sight of him. He stood rock-still, unable to speak. At that moment, his mother's smiling face was somehow all mixed up in his mind with the smiling face that used to appear in the night when he was a boy.

"Doctor," Nurse Ozaki cried, "Your mother wasn't injured at all. She was in the dugout the whole time."

"Son, you are all right, aren't you?" his mother asked.

And still he could not speak. He was not even aware of the tears on his face. His mother smiled again, and reached out a hand to touch his arm. He could scarcely believe that she was really safe. He saw that Nurse Ozaki had turned away tactfully, and at last he found words.

"How?" he blurted out. "Tell me what happened!"

It was really quite simple, she explained. After his father had gone to work that morning, she had chatted with the people working on the farm next door and had even joined them for a short time with their weeding. When the air-raid siren had sounded, she had entered the dugout with them. After the alert all-clear rang, the others had returned to their work in the fields. But suddenly she felt very tired and had decided to rest awhile in the dugout. So she had been seated at the entrance of the dugout at two minutes after eleven when she heard the whirring of planes overhead. At that point, she had moved farther inside. Then there was "white lightning and terrific blast." She had not been subject to either the heat or blast waves. But, as smoke began to flow into the shelter, she had been forced to climb outside. There, as she looked around, she trembled at the awful change in the world. A huge ball of smoke was rising above the Urakami district, and she immediately thought, "What's happened to my son?" When she saw the scores of buildings in flames and the columns of smoke coming from the hospital, she was sure that he had been injured, perhaps killed.

But now they were reunited. Silently, they smiled at each other, and he wondered at how sweet life could be—for some people at least. Mother and son, who had been lost to each other beyond the shadow of a doubt, had found each other.

"Have you heard any word about Father?" he asked and saw her expression sadden.

"No, nothing," she said slowly. "But the explosion was here, not in downtown Nagasaki. I'm sure he is all right."

"Of course he is," he said, instantly reassured. Then he turned to the others. "Say, let's eat. We could all use a little food." He was aware all at once of his empty stomach and that he had not had anything to eat all day. And since the bomb had gone off just as the patients had been about to eat their first meal of the day, they were undoubtedly in the same condition, as were the hospital personnel. He saw the expressions of the others turn to anticipation and brightness.

There was a brick wall, separating the compounds of the seminary school and the hospital proper, which had been knocked down. With the available bricks, seminary student Noguchi built a furnace for cooking. The hospital was still burning, but earlier Brother Mizuiwa, despite the protests of staff personnel, had managed to reach the kitchen at the edge of the basement and carry out some of the foodstocks.

In a remarkably short time, Dr. Sakurai was able to begin

serving the patients rice balls and vegetable soup. After they had eaten came the weary hospital personnel. Then, as there was much left over, he began passing it out to the dozens of injured people who had sought comfort there. Among them were arms factory workers, students in the Patriotic Corps, and people in the neighborhood whose houses had been destroyed. It was a strange place for a meal—alongside a hospital in flames and with a background of moans from the more seriously injured. Yet stomachs were soon full and spirits rose.

And it made him think of the basic principles of life. The hospital, the X-ray equipment, tens of thousands of books, irreplaceable equipment—all were burning. The personal possessions, the clothes, the prized and intimate individual treasures would soon be ashes. But what of those things? What of the X-ray equipment? What of the building? Weren't most of them alive? Hadn't they escaped the deadly scythe? And wasn't that what really mattered?

The emotion-packed meal came to an end. Dusk had begun to surround them, and Dr. Sakurai realized that something would have to be done to prepare for the night ahead. Makeshift beds probably should be built for some of the seriously injured patients to sleep on. It was a formidable job. There were now nearly a hundred people to be cared for by a working staff of six. He finally came to the conclusion that they just didn't have the time to construct beds. Perhaps the most seriously wounded could be moved to a more comfortable place instead. But where?

He remembered the small brick building just behind the hospital which was used for food storage. Maybe they could remove the bales of rice from that building and put several patients there. He asked Nurse Ozaki to take charge of that project, and she nodded and quickly began to recruit help.

Once more he took the long walk to the little glen beyond the river where Dr. Miyazaki was resting. She seemed better now, and after he had rebandaged her face, he and Brother Mizuiwa half-carried her back to the hospital. Next came Mr. Kinoshita who by now had turned almost black from his burns and was gasping for breath. Medical student Kawano carried the injured teacher on his back, wading across the river and trudging through the fields to the hospital. Mrs. Kinoshita, with the baby on her back, followed close behind, sobbing all the way.

More perplexing was the problem of transporting the seriously-injured Tsujimoto couple across the river. Brother Mizuiwa and Mr. Kawano tried to lift Mr. Tsujimoto, but his great weight was too much even for them. Then his daughter and brother-in-law appeared, bringing a wooden door from a wrecked house. Using that as a stretcher, Mizuiwa and Noguchi, helped by others, were able to carry the wounded man to the hospital. Dr. Sakurai had little hope for Mr. Tsujimoto when he compared the now-pitiful figure, moaning and writhing on the improvised stretcher, with the hearty man he had seen early that morning.

It must have been close to eight, for darkness was closing in, when the doctor saw a stooped, solitary figure walking slowly down the hill to the right of the hospital. The form looked vaguely familiar, and he moved out the gate toward it. When the man saw Dr. Sakurai's silhouette in front of the gate, he seemed to falter for an instant, then moved resolutely forward. About twenty feet away he stopped and held out his hands. "Son?" he called softly. "Son? Is that you?"

Dr. Sakurai gasped and ran toward the old man. "Father!" he cried and his arms encircled the frail body. "We were worried when you did not appear. What happened?"

What had happened to Dr. Sakurai's father had been typical of what happened to many old people that day. He had not been injured physically but he had been emotionally stunned. That morning he had been working at the court in the center of the old city. When the bomb had exploded, he had run outside, certain that it must have been dropped nearby. But he quickly saw that the damage was neither serious nor widespread in the immediate area. Most of the houses remained upright, though a few caught fire. Someone shouted that the bomb must have exploded over the area from Urakami Station to the Urakami Cathedral, and his eyes widened when he thought of his wife's and son's whereabouts.

He set out at once in that direction. But he could not pass through one neighborhood directly in his path because of the intense fire there. Instead, he circled to the north around the devastated area hoping to reach Mt. Kompira which rose steeply behind the hospital. When he had made the painful climb to the top, pausing often to rest his aching legs and straining lungs, he paused and gazed in astonishment at the scene below him. The two-mile-square area was a fiery sea, with the Urakami district the worst hit of all. At that moment, he was sure that neither his wife nor his son, on the edge of that circle of death, could possibly have survived. He sank to the ground, horrified at the absolute destruction that lay before him. He stared, unable to tear his eyes away from the dreadful scene. At last, he fell asleep.

It was nearly dark when he awoke. For an instant, he did not know where he was. Then he remembered and rose and picked his way carefully down the mountainside toward the corpses he fully expected to find. As he descended, the smoke grew increasingly thick and the odor of charred material grew stronger. People seriously burned and in great pain passed by him, striving to reach the top of the mountain.

"What happened down there?" he called at one point. But the only response was a glazed look and often a cry, "Help me." What could he do anyway? he thought, but he needn't have worried. The people continued on their blind way without stopping.

When he reached the bottom of the hill and what had once been a heavily-populated area, the smoke from the burning buildings made it difficult for him to breathe. Here, almost nothing was left standing; bodies of people lay sprawled everywhere, and he was more convinced than ever that his wife and son could not have lived through this. But he had to find out for sure. And so he finally reached the Nagasaki First Branch Hospital, and found his son, and a few minutes later, his wife.

"Well, not injured, eh?" he said with a calmness he did not feel. Then, as tears stung his eyes, a great joy suddenly filled his heart and choked his throat. "I could not ever again hope for such a miracle as seeing you both alive and well," he said with a great effort. Then his eyes were drawn to a couple lying on the ground, two people groaning in agony and terribly burned. He saw that it was Mr. and Mrs. Tsujimoto, close friends of theirs, and was saddened despite his own good fortune.

A young man approached, stood looking down at the suffering couple, then abruptly pressed his fists to his eyes. Dr. Sakurai, recognizing their eldest son, Yokichi, walked over and put his hand on the young man's shoulder. The young man was sobbing, and murmuring, "If only I had been here. If only . . ."

"It wouldn't have helped them," Dr. Sakurai said gently.

Yokichi had been a hundred miles away at eleven that morning, working in Fukuoka. It had been just after lunch that he had heard over the radio that a new-type bomb had been dropped on Nagasaki. He had immediately run to the railroad station and a half hour later had boarded a train bound for home.

At least ten miles outside of Nagasaki, he began seeing demolished houses, and guessed that if damage had been inflicted this far out, the city must indeed have been wiped off the face of the earth. He was wrong. What he was seeing was a consequence of topography. The bomb had exploded over the bowl-shaped city, and the surrounding hills had reflected much of the blast effects inward. But the gully through which the railroad tracks passed provided an outlet through which blast waves raced outward for miles, smashing everything in their way.

At Michinoo Station, two stops short of Nagasaki, he was told he must get off the train. The next two stations—at Urakami and in Nagasaki proper—had been badly damaged. So he climbed down and joined the other passengers who were also there to search for family members and relatives. They all stared at the vast destruction about them with unbelieving eyes.

The young man began walking around the mountain toward Oka Village where his own wife and two children lived. He crossed the railroad tracks and was astonished to see that even the solid wooden ties were burning. He moved on and it got even worse. Everywhere there seemed to be smoke and flames and scores of injured and frightened people who did not know where to go.

Oka had been almost wiped out. Everything was on fire, including his own ruined house. There was no sign of his wife or his children, and he was sure that they must have been killed instantly. At that moment, he almost gave up. What was the point of going on? But somehow his feet acted on their own and took him toward the Motohara neighborhood where his parents lived. That area had been almost as badly damaged. Where could he look now? Then he thought of the Nagasaki First Branch Hospital, and it was there that he found his parents, alive but both horribly injured. It was obvious that these once sturdy people could not last much longer.

"Don't give up hope," Dr. Sakurai advised him gently. Together, the two men, with some help, carried the elderly couple into the food-storage building and laid them down in the corner.

"Isn't there some medicine you can give them?" Yokichi asked.

"The hospital is still burning," the doctor answered. "We will have to wait until the morning."

The young man sat down and gave his parents some water, tenderly trickling it into their blistered mouths. Even the water, he noticed, had a strange burnt smell. He looked up at Dr. Sakurai, at the lines of pain and sadness in the doctor's thin face. "You have been very kind," he whispered.

"I wish there were more I could do."

Yokichi bent his head. He, like his parents, was a devout Catholic. Now he began to pray: "Jesus, Mary, Joseph . . . Pray for us . . ." Though a Buddhist, Dr. Sakurai lowered his head too. What else can man do, he thought, other than pray? And it is all to one and the same God.

In a short while, Dr. Sakurai left the room to check on his colleague, Dr. Miyazaki. She was lying by the wall in the yard, and she too had visitors. Her 70-year-old mother and her eldest brother had walked all the way down through the Nishiyama mountain pass to find out how she had fared. Along the way, they had come upon the fires and had seen the groups of people fleeing from the holocaust. At this moment, Dr. Miyazaki's mother was looking with concern at her daughter, whose face was almost entirely covered by bandages.

"I'm sorry she was injured," Dr. Sakurai said. "Somehow I feel that it was my fault."

The old lady seemed not to hear him. She continued to study her injured daughter. But the brother turned to Dr. Sakurai. "She should be honored that she was injured while on duty," he said stiffly. Somehow it sounded as if he were trying to convince himself.

Dr. Sakurai went to the center of the yard and told the people assembled there, "Sleep tonight wherever you can and wrap yourselves up in anything available."

"But we don't have any quilts," someone shouted back.

At his sheepish look and mumbled words, "I'm really sorry about that," some of the patients broke into laughter. Immediately after the explosion, when a few patients had paused to gather up clothes or quilts to take with them, he had warned, "Don't carry anything on your back. It's too risky. Leave everything behind." Years before he had read an account of the great Kanto earthquake in 1923 and he remembered that many people who had been carrying their belongings on their backs had died when the cloth caught fire. But on this morning the patients who had followed his advice had no blankets for the night, while those who had ignored him had their quilts with them.

Darkness descended upon them. It had been a long, long day, and it was not over yet. Around him sprawled those people who had managed, so far at least, to survive that long day. From nearby came cries from the baby Mr. Kawano had brought there. The young man ran to get some water, brought it to the child and he quieted instantly. Someone suddenly called, "Mr. Tanaka. Where are you, Mr. Tanaka?" A voice answered in the darkness and there was silence again. Snores came loudly from near the wall. That would be Brother Mizuiwa, thought Dr. Sakurai. He was probably exhausted from the great labors he had performed that day.

Mrs. Kinoshita tottered up to him, obviously in pain.

"Doctor," she gasped, "I know you must be tired, but can you look at my husband? He is suffering so."

He went at once to Mr. Kinoshita and discovered that his condition was growing worse by the minute. "I'm afraid I can't do anything for him," he told the sobbing woman. Close by were Mr. and Mrs. Tsujimoto, with their son standing beside them, praying. The elderly couple were also suffering and in great pain. Dr. Sakurai felt helpless that he had nothing to relieve their pain. He turned away as the son's words followed him . . . "Jesus, Mary and Joseph, we entrust his spirit and soul to your hands . . . Jesus, Mary and Joseph, help us at his last suffering . . ."

There was a muffled cry and he turned in time to see Mr. Tsujimoto convulse violently, then go limp. "He has breathed his last," his son wailed. Dr. Sakurai stared at the dead man, the first from the hospital that he had lost, and felt sick at heart. He had been unable to do one thing to save him.

He walked outside the gate and looked at burning Nagasaki. After a few minutes, someone came up behind him and he turned and saw Nurse Ozaki. "Miss Ozaki . . . I . . . want to thank you for . . . your great help. I only wish . . . that I had been able to do more for them."

She looked at him, and her eyes glistened in the firelight. "You did everything that any man could possibly do."

Before he could answer, he heard the sound of planes and wondered for a moment whether they were more American bombers. But he really didn't care very much. The damage had been done. What else could possibly happen to them?

What Dr. Sakurai was hearing was the final irony. In a grim error by American military propagandists, thousands of additional leaflets were even then fluttering down on the devastated city urging the citizens to evacuate before Nagasaki was destroyed.

Dr. Sakurai and his nurse stood side by side, staring

silently at the ruined city. He wondered how many people had died in the holocaust and how many were still lying somewhere out there, injured and helpless. This is war, he thought, total war. This is what war really means. On the hillside across the valley the tiny fires on the slopes seemed to blink malevolently at him like a thousand angry, red eyes.

CHAPTER 19

The Agony Ends

IN THE MORNING, WHEN DR. SAKURAI AWOKE, A TIREDNESS HUNG on him like a shroud. The few hours of sleep he had had on the hard ground had not helped much. He squinted up into the cloudless sky and thought of the dream he had just had. Somehow in his tumbling subconscious, Nagasaki had got all mixed up with Pompeii and what they had in common was that each city and the people who lived there had been buried deep beneath the ashes, rocks and fallen structures. In the morning air, still smoky and pungent, it seemed the bad dream was true.

He lifted himself on his elbows and looked toward the still smoking ruins of the Nagasaki First Branch Hospital. That was reality enough, and an ugly reality at that. And when he thought of the medical equipment, the furnishings, all sorts of medical supplies, the medical books and notes that had been accumulated over the years—that had all by now been reduced to ashes—he knew for a certainty that it was no dream. He was right back where he started, penniless, without equipment or a place to work.

He shook his head to clear away the discouraging thoughts and stood up. Enough of self-pity! There was a great difference between the young man of a few years ago and the tested, experienced doctor he was today. And there was still work to be done. Right at this moment there were nearly seventy patients with no homes to return to who had to be cared for. There was Mr. Kinoshita and the recently widowed Mrs. Tsujimoto, both seriously burned and bedridden in the emergency food-storage room. Dr. Miyazaki's face had been badly lacerated and needed an antiseptic covering, and Father Kawamoto, with two black eyes, had a severe concussion. And there were at least two dozen other serious burn cases, as well as a score of blast-injured victims. Lastly, there were his regular in-patients, though fortunately none of them had been critically ill at the time of the explosion. Still, he had to do something for those who required treatment. Although he was without medical equipment, medicines or medical books, he was still a doctor.

Nurse Ozaki greeted him. "Good morning. Did you sleep well?"

"Yes. Well enough. And you?"

Again, there was that silent smile. "Oh, very well, thank you."

"You look . . ." He hesitated. "You look . . . rested this morning."

She lowered her head shyly and murmured: "I should get the breakfast started." Then, like a frightened doe, she darted away. He watched her rouse several of the staff, and together they started making the fires to cook the rice.

There was no more time for personal thoughts. Suffering and despair still existed. The people to whom he had promised to give "some medicine tomorrow" had already begun to call out plaintively to him for help. But where was he to find medicine? The city was still burning, and he began to wonder if everything in Nagasaki was on fire. Where could he turn?

"Doctor, Doctor," called seminary student Noguchi. "Can you please come here a moment?"

Dr. Sakurai hurried over to the young man, who led him to the basement hallway in front of the kitchen. In that area were a coal bin, another food-storage compartment and a dugout.

"We have to go in there," the young man said, indicating the dugout. "There's something I want to show you."

The doctor nodded, and as he stepped inside, hot air swept over him and he recoiled instinctively. Then he realized that the upstairs must still be smoldering, like hot coals in an old fire. Once inside the dugout, Mr. Noguchi gestured toward the inner corner where two crude wooden crates sat. "Medicine," he said, pointing proudly.

"Medicine!" the doctor said unbelievingly. "But how is that possible?"

It turned out that Mr. Noguchi had been very farsighted indeed. During the past week, he had brought medical supplies little by little into the safe dugout, "just in case," as he put it. "I would have brought them to you yesterday," he said, "but the fire was too intense."

"But we have them now!" the doctor cried jubilantly, "thanks to you. How clever you have been!"

Together, the two men moved the small crates out of the steamy dugout. Once outside, they opened them. First, the doctor found gauze and bandages, and underneath Anesthesin, chloramine, Mercurochrome, and various pills. Though the contents of the crates were not complete in any sense, they were much more than what he had expected to find upon awakening that morning. Now, holding the bandages and medicines in his hands, he felt a surge of hope. Once again, he had the tools to relieve pain, to sterilize and to bandage.

At exactly eight o'clock on the morning of August 10, in the smoking ruins of the Nagasaki First Branch Hospital, he began seeing patients. Mr. Noguchi and others had found a room, partially salvageable, and had cleared away the debris and set up a table. The most serious cases came first. They brought in Mr. Kinoshita who had been quietly enduring his pain in the food-storage room throughout the night. The doctor sprinkled Anesthesin over his face, shoulders and chest, all of which had been burned and was blackly inflamed. Over the whole area, he then carefully wrapped gauze. He doubted that it would do much good. A doctor's rule of thumb is that if burns cover less than one-third of the surface of the body, the patient's life can probably be saved. In Mr. Kinoshita's case the burns covered nearly half the body surface.

Still, when Mrs. Kinoshita asked him anxiously, "Doctor, will he be all right?" he had to reply, "I think so, but it will be a bad two or three days." He knew full well that the medicine he had applied would only alleviate the pain. It was certainly not a permanent cure for burns of such severity. But when he looked at the wife, eating her heart out with worry, he could not give her any other answer.

The next patient was 60-year-old Mrs. Tsujimoto who had been working in the rice-paddy field with her late husband when the bomb exploded. Strangely, her inflamed burns were located in specific and contradictory places—on the face, the back, and the backs of the legs. The reason soon became clear. Her back and the backs of her legs were so affected because she had been bending over, away from the blast, at the time. Her face had been burned when she looked over her shoulder at the sky, startled by the sound of planes which had preceded the "lightning flash." As he had done with Mr. Kinoshita, Dr. Sakurai treated her with gauze and Anesthesin. Mrs. Tsujimoto, though obviously in great pain, remained silent. Her husband had died in agony just the night before. His remains were now being cremated by Brother Mizuiwa, and she was unable to attend the ceremony of the man with whom she had spent most of her life. She was probably suffering more from the death and funeral of her husband than from her own painful wounds.

He had just finished treating Mrs. Tsujimoto when a stocky, middle-aged woman rushed up to him and said, "Doctor, please come and see my husband. He has been badly injured."

Nurse Ozaki said quickly, "The doctor has patients here who need his help." But when the woman started to cry, Nurse Ozaki turned to the doctor with a helpless expression.

"I'd better go," he said quietly, then turned to the woman. "Where is your husband?"

Her crying stopped at once. "Just below the hospital, about fifty yards away," she said hopefully. "It won't take long at all."

Although there were many patients still to be treated, he did not hesitate, but followed the woman out the shattered doorway. The patients waiting in the yard stared at him with expressions varying from surprise to resentment. "Be right back," he called cheerfully, and passed through the gate.

It was the first time he had traveled away from the hospital, toward Nagasaki. As he walked down the hill—it was considerably more than fifty yards, he noted—he observed that very little was still standing.

There was no longer a road for them to walk on; the dirt and grass had melted together, baked into a dull brown clay, and the walls, which had lined the road and divided the house plots, had been twisted flat.

The woman led him to a spot behind the remains of a stone wall where a thin man lay sheltered by pieces of boards. Upon seeing the doctor, he said weakly, "I was hit by the bomb while I was working at the arms factory."

Dr. Sakurai examined the man, who was not seriously injured, although he had a three-inch gash in his forehead.

The doctor treated the wound with Mercurochrome, bandaged it and assured the woman that her husband would be all right. But he wasn't that sure. He was puzzled by the extreme paleness of the man's skin, a look he had seen before and had not understood. But the words "radiation poisoning" meant nothing to him. So he could not know that this same man would be dead in three days.

He spied an aged woman, with ruffled, unkempt hair walking slowly toward them, the stick in her hand helping her to pick her path through the litter. "Doctor," she called, "we need you." It was Mr. Kinoshita's aged mother, and as she drew nearer, he saw dozens of tiny cuts on her face.

"Let me fix those cuts," he said, rising and going to meet her.

She waved her stick impatiently. "Never mind about me. It's my husband, Mr. Kinoshita, who needs help." He was about to tell her of her son at the hospital, but she had already started back toward town. He followed her to the family's pottery shop, which was their residence as well. It had been almost completely destroyed, and he climbed over the fallen pillars and tiles until she brought him to Mr. Isematsu Kinoshita. He lay beneath a canopy of boards, his clothes in tatters, holding his head. He too had been working in a paddy field when the bomb exploded. Luckily he had been near a stone wall and had flung himself behind it in time to escape the direct effects of the rays, but the wall had shattered and he had been hit in the face with the dislodged stones. His face was cut, swollen and purple. Furthermore, he seemed to have lost all spirit and energy.

Dr. Sakurai cleaned the open scratches on the old man's face and gave him some pills to ease the pain. Mr. Kinoshita did not respond, apparently unaware of what was going on. His wife told Dr. Sakurai that her husband was deeply concerned over the whereabouts of his two remaining children. Neither his son nor his daughter, a teacher at Shiroyama

Primary School, had yet been located and he feared for their safety. His eldest son had gone to war and Mr. Kinoshita had just been informed that he had been killed on the battlefield. When Dr. Sakurai told the old woman that he had treated her badly burned son only that morning, and that he had doubts about the young man's survival, she gasped and put her hand to her mouth.

"I cannot tell that to Mr. Kinoshita," she whispered. "Already his mind . . . it has been affected. This would unhinge him completely."

"I'm sorry. But your son is still alive."

"I will come and see him as soon as I can leave my husband."

He nodded, turned and made his way slowly up the hill. When he reached the hospital, tired and hungry, the patients sitting and lying on the ground immediately sought his attention. Silently, he examined them one by one. The most seriously injured was a TB patient who had a glass splinter on the side of his neck. He was gasping for breath, and Dr. Sakurai tried to ascertain whether the gasping was caused by sputum in the throat or by the glass splinter. Luckily, he discovered that it was the former, and a few deft swabs solved the problem.

He stood up and rubbed his eyes. It had happened again. For the last hour or so, he had been conscious of a strange phenomenon in himself: He seemed constantly on the edge of tears. At certain moments—bending over a patient, walking along a road, or just chatting with someone—his eyes would suddenly fill and he would have to wipe away the blurred images. There was no reason for it, none at all. Yet he felt that if someone said a harsh word to him, he would have burst into tears. It was very strange. It had never happened to him before.

Nurse Ozaki came to him and said: "Doctor, there's a young man here I think you should look at. I don't know how long he has been here. No one seems to have seen him before now."

She led him to a concrete strip outside the wall not far from the gate, and he saw a young man lying there. He had passed not more than six feet from the prone figure several times, and had never noticed him. This 20-year-old had been a student at the Nagasaki Medical College and when the building he had been in had crashed down like a house of blocks, he had crawled out of the wreckage and managed to climb up to the hospital. Once he had reached this spot, however, he had collapsed, exhausted.

Dr. Sakurai started toward him and bent over. But before he could touch him, the young man opened his eyes, murmured, "Hello, Father," smiled sadly—and died. Once again, Dr. Sakurai's eyes unaccountably filled with tears.

He moved slowly back to the yard, and Brother Mizuiwa came up to him with a request. He wanted to start work immediately on the chapel. Could he ask some of the less injured people there to help him? Dr. Sakurai stared at him in astonishment. In all those vast ruins, one person was already anxious to start the rebuilding process. At that moment, he marveled at man's tenacity, the drive to struggle upright after an almost fatal body blow.

He nodded his head and watched in wonder as Brother Mizuiwa and five or six others began clearing away the rubble that covered the chapel area. These patients, like most people, were injured and knew nothing of the fate of their families. They had lost all they possessed, their houses, personal effects, perhaps loved ones. Yet they put aside self-pity and started the task of reconstructing their chapel. To Dr. Sakurai, it was a wondrous testament to human courage.

As the day progressed, his own work increased. In the afternoon, many more injured people came to the hospital, perhaps in the belief that doctors were available there to help them. Brother Mizuiwa and Mr. Noguchi built a treatment center in a corner of the yard. It was really a makeshift clinic made of four bamboo poles, brought in by a parent of a patient, and covered with cloth. Mr. Noguchi carried in a table and chairs which his friends had found, and Dr. Sakurai removed the medical supplies there. The whole thing resembled a battlefield hospital, which, in fact, it was. Dr. Sakurai, assisted by medical student Kawano, began treating the patients. The nurses helped as much as they could, but they had to cook rice and soup and distribute the food to the patients.

Then came another sad interruption. Nurse Ozaki rushed into the tent, carrying a baby. As Mr. Kawano stood weeping, his new son cried, "Mama, Mama," and slipped away. Dr. Sakurai watched, helpless. What could he have done that he had not done to save this young life? He clenched his fists in frustration, but at the same time he was beginning to realize that this was but another example of the strange malady that seemed to accompany the new bomb.

He had hardly faced that shock, when Nurse Ozaki presented him with another, telling him that Mr. Kinoshita had left the hospital. "He said he wanted to be with his parents at the end," she explained sadly. Dr. Sakurai thought of going after the desperately injured man, then gave up the idea. There was nothing more he could do for the poor schoolteacher anyhow.

An hour later, Mr. Tomimura, an official of the Nagasaki Town Association, arrived, just at mealtime, and Dr. Sakurai asked him to share their simple meal. But the older man said he was too excited to eat.

"Doctor, have you heard that Japan has used a new type of bomb against America? Our country has also taken back Okinawa, Kiska Island and Saipan by means of this new weapon. Our combined fleet has now gone out to finish the job."

Dr. Sakurai looked at the older man with something akin

to awe. He was aware that often when man is down and out, he has to find solace in wishful thinking. But the town official's words were ridiculous. How, amidst the devastation that surrounded them, could the other man actually believe such folly? Dr. Sakurai lost his patience. "We've had enough of it, haven't we?" he said with sudden revulsion. "Even if a new type of bomb has been dropped on the Americans, I wouldn't be able to find any satisfaction in such an act. It would accomplish nothing, and I, for one, have no more stomach for the useless killing of man by man."

The town official left hurriedly, shaking his head over such treacherous utterings. His day, and the day of others like him, is just about over, thought the doctor. We started the whole thing and now we are paying for it. But maybe we—indeed the whole world—can learn a great lesson from it, that nothing in the end is ever accomplished when man resorts to violence.

That night after supper, he went again to little knoll outside the gate, and once again Nurse Ozaki joined him there. They did not speak, for they had no need for words. For the first time, he was able to see their relationship in personal, man-woman terms.

What would it be like for him without her? he wondered. What if she already had been his wife, and at a single stroke had been taken from him? He could imagine waking up in the middle of the night and finding the other half of the bed empty and cold, then getting up and prowling about the house, but finding each room empty of her presence. He might sit and wonder where she was, where she had gone, until he would know with a painful rush that her absence was permanent. He could almost feel her direct loss and now he could understand the lost look on the faces of so many of the people he had encountered.

As the two silent people watched, two steel girders in the Mitsubishi Steelworks below them and far away, melted through and collapsed with a muffled crash. In a way, he thought, the crash symbolized Nagasaki's final tragedy. From this moment on, the situation could not get much worse; it could only improve. The destruction was ended and the rebuilding would begin. In the shattered street below the hospital, cremation ceremonies for Mr. Kinoshita had begun. That ritual would be enacted many times in the weeks and months to follow, for the dying would continue as the radiation took its toll. But the fiery blowtorch was extinguished. Nagasaki's searing moment of agony was over.

That same night on the island of Tinian, Captain Parsons sent the following top-secret message to General Groves and Dr. Oppenheimer:

OPERATION CENTERBOARD

On Aug. 11, we will start assembly of two additional FMs [Fat Mans]. On Aug. 12, we will complete assembly of F101 and continue F102. On Aug. 13 we can drop F101, continue assembly F102, commence assembly F103. On Aug. 16, F102 can be dropped.

But additional bombs were not necessary, and General Groves ordered further production discontinued. The destruction of Nagasaki ended the war.

"This is the nearest thing to Doomsday that one could possibly imagine. I am sure that at the end of the world—in the last millisecond of the earth's existence—the last man will see what we just saw."

—DR. GEORGE KISTIAKOWSKY, ONE OF THE DEVELOPERS OF "FAT MAN"

Epilogue

From the diary of Professor Raisuke Shirabe of the Nagasaki Medical College:

August 11. TWO DAYS HAVE PASSED SINCE THE BIG BOMB WAS DROPPED ON US, AND I STILL CAN FIND NO EXPLANATION AS TO WHY PEOPLE CONTINUE TO DIE. MANY OF THEM HAVE NO VISIBLE INJURIES, YET MOST EXHIBIT THE SAME SYMPTOMS: BLEEDING FROM THE GUMS, LOSS OF APPETITE, FEVER, APATHY, THE BEGINNING OF LOSS OF HAIR, BLOODY DIARRHEA—THEN DEATH. WHAT IS THIS STRANGE, INVISIBLE KILLER THAT REMAINS IN OUR MIDST?

YET EVEN IF WE WERE ABLE TO DIAGNOSE AND TREAT PROPERLY, WE DO NOT HAVE THE TOOLS. WITH THE UNIVERSITY, OUR HOSPITAL, AND MANY OF THE OTHERS DESTROYED, WE HAVE NO WORKSHOP, NO MEDICINE OR EQUIPMENT. AFTER CONSULTING WITH DEAN TSUNOO, WHO HAS HIMSELF BEEN SERIOUSLY WOUNDED, IT HAS BEEN DECIDED TO RECRUIT WORKERS TO REPAIR THE CIVIC HALL OF IWAYA AND WORK HAS ALREADY STARTED. BY TOMORROW MORNING WE SHOULD BE ABLE TO HOSPITALIZE FIFTY OF THE MOST BADLY INJURED THERE. NO WORD YET ABOUT MY SONS, SEIICHI OR KOJI. I FEAR THEY ARE BOTH DEAD. THANK GOD THAT I PERSUADED THE REST OF MY FAMILY TO MOVE OUTSIDE THE CITY . . .

August 13. ON MY WAY HOME, I RAN INTO MR. BABA WHO SAID THAT ONE OF MY SONS HAD RETURNED HOME. HE DID NOT KNOW WHICH ONE IT WAS. IT WAS SEIICHI, I DISCOVERED WHEN I REACHED THE HOUSE, BUT ABOUT ONE-THIRD OF HIS BODY HAD BEEN BURNED. I TREATED HIM AS BEST I COULD WITH GLUCOSE AND ALCOHOL. UNDER THE CIRCUMSTANCES, HE SEEMED IN GOOD SPIRITS, BUT LATE THAT EVENING HE BEGAN TO EXHIBIT THOSE SAME MYSTERIOUS SYMPTOMS. I HAD ALREADY NOTED THAT WITH THOSE VICTIMS IN NAMESHI VILLAGE WHO HAD BLACK SPOTS ON THEIR SKIN DEATH WAS VIRTUALLY CERTAIN. WHY? NO MATTER HOW HARD I TRIED TO ANALYZE THE CAUSE OF THEIR DEATH, MY MEDICAL KNOWLEDGE WAS INSUFFICIENT TO PROVIDE AN ANSWER. NOW SEIICHI, TOO, HAS THOSE BLACK SPOTS. I FEAR GREATLY FOR HIM. AND STILL NO WORD ABOUT KOJI . . .

September 1. SO MUCH HAS HAPPENED IN THE LAST THREE WEEKS. ON AUGUST 15 JAPAN SURRENDERED, AND A DAY LATER MY SON SEIICHI DIED. DEAR SEIICHI, WHOSE IGNORANT FATHER WAS NOT EVEN ABLE TO TELL HIS WIFE WHAT HER SON HAD DIED OF! ON AUGUST 18, THE AMERICAN FORCES LANDED AND WERE SOON FOLLOWED BY TEAMS OF SCIENTIFIC AND MEDICAL INVESTIGATORS. WE LEARNED FOR THE FIRST TIME THE NAME OF THE INVISIBLE KILLER—ATOMIC RADIATION, WHICH ATTACKS BLOOD CORPUSCLES. WHAT WAS USED ON NAGASAKI WAS IN FACT AN ATOMIC BOMB, A HORRIBLE NEW WEAPON WITH WHICH MAN CAN NOW DESTROY HIMSELF JUST AS WE HAVE BEEN DESTROYED.

NEAR THE END OF THE MONTH, I AND MY WIFE AND THREE DAUGHTERS WENT TO THE REMAINS OF THE MEDICAL SCHOOL TO MAKE A FINAL SEARCH FOR OUR MISSING SON, KOJI. PERCHED ON THE RUINS THERE WAS A FLOCK OF CROWS LOOKING FOR ROTTING FLESH. WE THREW STONES TO CHASE THEM AWAY AND THEY SQUAWKED ANGRILY AT THE INTERRUPTION. NEAR THE LARGEST PILE OF RUBBLE WAS A HEAP OF WHITE BONES. I IMAGINED THAT THE STUDENTS, TRAPPED UNDER THE FALLEN ROOF, HAD TRIED TO ESCAPE IN A GROUP. BUT THEY HAD FAILED AND HAD DIED TOGETHER IN ONE SPOT.

FOR A LONG TIME WE STOOD LOOKING AT THE MISERABLE SIGHT, ANGUISHED BY THE THOUGHT THAT THE REMAINS OF KOJI MIGHT BE THERE. THEN OUR DAUGHTER JUNKO, WHO WAS IN THE MIDDLE OF THE RUINED AUDITORIUM, CRIED OUT: "FATHER, COME HERE QUICKLY! I'VE FOUND SOMETHING."

MY WIFE AND I RAN OVER TO SEE WHAT JUNKO HAD FOUND. THEN IT WAS MY WIFE'S TURN TO CRY OUT: "THAT'S KOJI'S SUIT!"

OVER A METAL DOOR IN THE MIDDLE OF THE RUINS LAY A TORN PIECE OF BLACK STUDENT TROUSERS WITH WHITE LINING. ON IT WE COULD CLEARLY SEE THE NAME "YAMAMOTO." THE TROUSERS HAD BEEN A PRESENT TO KOJI FROM MY SISTER'S FAMILY.

UNTIL THAT MOMENT THERE HAD BEEN A FAINT HOPE IN MY HEART THAT KOJI WOULD SOMEHOW BE ALL RIGHT. NOW THAT HOPE WAS GONE. FIRST SEIICHI, THEN KOJI, BOTH WERE NOW DEAD. THE FRUIT OF MY SEED WAS NO MORE.

WITH THE CLOTH IN HAND, I STOOD AMIDST THE RUINS, MOTIONLESS AND SAPPED OF THE SPIRIT THAT HAD SO FAR SUSTAINED ME. I BOWED MY HEAD. *Namu Amidadutsu.* MAY YOUR SOUL REMAIN UNTROUBLED. *Namu Amidadutsu* . . .

DURING THOSE SAME WEEKS, MANY PEOPLE LAMENTED AND endured as did Dr. Shirabe. Thousands died within days of Terrible Thursday, bewildered and beset by that unknown ravager, and finally not caring what became of them. Cremations took place throughout the day and night. Some people survived initially, only to succumb mysteriously three or four weeks later. A few gave up hope—for themselves or their loved ones—only to find joy in an inexplicable recovery. Others came to realize several months or even years afterward that they had only been borrowing on death's final payment. The collector was usually leukemia.

Yet in those first weeks what life remained persevered and tried to adapt. Makeshift huts sprang up throughout the city, where groups of survivors clung to the life that was meagerly theirs. The emergency food distribution program was in full swing and gradually medical teams were organized to treat the victims.

A week after the explosion an attempt was made to turn on the water supply in the bombed-out area, but the system was so leaky that it had to be shut off again. Repairs were exceedingly difficult to make, for of the whole public works construction crew, only three men put in an appearance after the bomb fell, and it took several days to locate the other survivors. But report they did, and went to work. The main road from Nagasaki to Omura was clogged with debris for nearly a mile and a half. Using rakes and shovels—no machinery was available—work crews cleared a path six-and-a-half feet wide, despite intense heat from the smoldering ruins. By the 15th it could take two-way traffic.

Although the city had suffered a near-mortal blow, nature was already beginning to reassert herself. Wheat began to sprout everywhere. A few of the grain storehouses had been blasted apart and the wheat grain drawn up into the sky. It came down all over the city, falling on the hot ground. Some burned up, but much of it took root in the fertile ash and grew. Near the medical school had been a field of clover. Bare after the explosion, the field slowly began to bloom once more. But there have been no four-leaf clovers; at least, no one has been able to find one.

Close by the ruins of the Fuji Shrine, a huge nettle tree three hundred years old was stripped of leaves and branches. Months of rain fell on the bare old trunk and the sun warmed it, but it never came back to life. Yet three weeks after the bomb fell, a morning glory at the foot of the dead tree was in full bloom. In other parts of the city, green buds began to emerge from that land where it was said that nothing would grow for seventy-five years. Even Mrs. Hamada's chickens, which had suddenly stopped producing, began laying eggs again in two weeks' time. But for a long while the egg whites all had a bluish cast to them. And in Mrs. Hamada's yard that part of her orange tree facing Urakami withered and for the next three years did not bear fruit. Then, without any reason, the entire tree was at once healthy and in full production.

The rebuilding began slowly as people emerged from despair into the sunlight. U. S. troops, occupying the country, were to assist in this slow rebirth, but by and large the citizens of Nagasaki were forced to fall back on their own resources in reconstructing their ruined homes, factories and public buildings. The central government, weak and impoverished after the war, was unable to help as much as it wanted to. In addition, there was the cruel irony that Japanese and world attention was—and still is—focused almost exclusively on Hiroshima. Nagasaki became the forgotten city, and it was common to hear the lament, "To be atom-bombed is bad, but to be second is worse."

Today Nagasaki is a monument to its citizens' hard work and sense of rededication. Once again ships built in Nagasaki dockyards ply the oceans, and though its traditional market, China, has dried up, the city has developed extensive trade with Singapore, Hong Kong, South Korea, West Germany and Burma. There are few scars in this bustling metropolis. The rebuilding has transformed the city and still goes on day after day.

Houses are creeping up the sides of the mountains now so that the hills appear to be covered with patchwork, multicolored tile. In the downtown section, skyscrapers are Japanese-style, eight and nine stories high, with boxlike windowless department stores. All this new construction has changed the old, quiet city of ginko trees and delicately fashioned gardens into a go-go city where the skyline is parted by smokestacks, high-rise apartments, power towers, TV antennae, and countless buildings atop which six-foot-high neon signs proclaim in English and Japanese: TOSHIBA—TAPE RECORDER, SANYO SANYO, GRAND HOTEL NAGASAKI . . .

The streets have all been widened and paved to accommodate the rush of new traffic. Today, there are cars of every make from many different countries, but they have one thing in common: They are all very small, and thus economical to operate. There are also trolley cars and buses, trucks, half-trucks, quarter-trucks, and motor bikes. And there are taxis. It has been said that Japan has more taxis per square mile than any country in the world, and you believe it when you notice that one out of every five cars passing by is a taxi.

Across Nagasaki Harbor to the west, the new Mitsubishi Shipyard seems to rise almost out of the water, looking much like a gigantic erector set with its skeleton steel structure. Behind the shipyard looms the bulk of Mt. Inasa with a huge master television antenna perched atop its 1,800-feet-high peak, the highest point in Nagasaki. Today there is also an observation tower on top of the mountain. It is a favorite spot for tourists, and throughout the day the little Nagasaki taxis speed wildly up the goat-path-wide mountain road so that visitors can see the new city of Nagasaki spread out in its entirety before them.

Food is no longer scarce in Nagasaki. Nowadays, wherever you walk in the city there are restaurants within a hundred feet of you—Japanese or Chinese restaurants mostly, with an occasional American, French, German, or Italian one. There are *sakabas* (Japanese bars) where you can get sake, Suntory whiskey, good Japanese beer, even Scotch and American bourbon, and there are *standobas* (stand-up bars) which offer "quickies." There are *kissaten,* where one may be served tea, coffee, pastry, and the specialty of Nagasaki, *castella,* a flat egg-sugar-butter-and-flour kind of sponge cake first brought to the old city hundreds of years ago by travelers from the Castillian section of Spain. There are shops selling candy, ice cream, and cakes, and ones selling meat, cigarettes, silks, and cameras. There are mammoth department stores, haberdashers, beauty salons, and jewelers. In the evening, tourists can visit Japanese night clubs where there are dancing partners, entertainers, singers, and showgirls—often imported from outside the country. There are food, drink, products, and pleasure aplenty now.

There are only three major reminders in the entire city of that day twenty-three years ago. One is in the old part of town, a two-story, white concrete building with a sign over the front door: "Atomic Bomb Casualty Commission." For the last twenty years, this joint U. S.-Japanese venture has been keeping track of the A-bomb survivors, of those victims who are still suffering and dying from the aftereffects of radiation. And since there were only two atomic bombs dropped on people in the current history of the world, Nagasaki provides unique statistics on what heat, blast, and radiation can do to humanity.

The second reminder is the giant bronze Peace Statue, a thirty-two-foot-high heroic male figure that dominates the knoll on which it stands. The right hand is lifted skyward as if threatening any future rain of destruction from above, while the left is stretched out horizontally in a traditional peace gesture. The eyes are closed in prayer for the dead. The statue was paid for almost entirely by donations from schoolchildren.

Near the statue stands the third reminder, a modernistic, concrete-and-stone building called the Nagasaki Cultural Center. Inside the well-lit, efficiently-run exhibit, a constant stream of visitors, including thousands upon thousands of uniformed schoolchildren who have been bused to that place from all over Japan, gaze in wonder and shock at such objects as:

—A pair of tattered, scorched work trousers and cap worn by a worker at the Mitsubishi Steelworks, 1,200 yards from Ground Zero.

—Three plastic reconstructions of keloidal scars * from burns on an arm, a leg, and a neck, the wounds showing muscles, tendons, and skin distorted and stretched away from the center of the scars.

* Scars with heavy raised scar tissue.

—A large piece of basalt rock covered on one side by small blisters, the result of the stone's beginning to bubble at 350 yards from Ground Zero.

—A metal helmet with the top of a human skull serving as a liner.

—A roll of iron wire fused into one solid mass at 1,000 yards from Ground Zero.

—A 3-by-15-feet strip of seared wallboard with a bright, inch-wide stripe running its entire length; it was part of the wall of a house which stood more than 3,000 yards away from Ground Zero. The light stripe was caused by a zinc drain pipe which hung down from the roof.

—A human hand and a large piece of glass fused into a single free-shape.

Queen Wilhelmina of the Netherlands is said to have fainted during her tour of the Cultural Center. The school-children seem more impressed with the view from the seventh floor.

It is quite a view with the little side streets meandering away from the hall. From that height you are not aware of how tightly-packed the houses are along those clean, narrow streets, how well-tended and neat the tiny flower gardens are. Once down to earth, however, the details stand out. Every now and then, between buildings, you come across a flight of stone steps leading up to the houses and inns on the hills above. These steps look as if someone has been pounding on them with a sledgehammer for years. They are cracked and broken and canted, with one side lifted as much as two feet out of line. The edges of the steps look as though they have been planed away, sliced off neatly by a diamond-hard scythe. And you glance back toward the Cultural Center, the approximate landmark of Ground Zero, and you calculate the distance from the steps to that site—about 900 yards.

Occasionally in this industrious community you can see a wrecked house—a pile of rubble, splintered wood, smashed window and door frames, split tiles, nothing standing higher than two feet—that has been neither rebuilt nor cleared away. And you wonder what happened to the owners of that particular home and why that lonely pile is still there. Perhaps the entire family perished that August day, and maybe the ruins just haven't been in anyone's way all these years.

A middle-aged woman approaches you on the street and somehow you cannot take your eyes off the dreadful keloid scar on her upper neck, a bloated, ugly, four-inch growth that distends her jawbone and pulls down one corner of her mouth into an involuntary sneer. She notices your eyes on her disfigurement and there is a slight slowing in her walk. You try to look away, but suddenly she smiles and her eyes are clear and warm. You find you are absurdly happy to be able to smile back at her.

In the small commemorative park near the Cultural Hall there is a rectangular plot at the head of which is a 12-foot-high stone monument. On it are inscribed the words: "This is the Epicenter of the Bomb. At 11:02 A.M. on August 9, 1945, an atomic bomb dropped from a B-29 exploded 500 meters in the air above this green stone pillar. By the blast and thermal rays exceeding 300,000 degrees Centigrade and the accompanying radioactivity the entire area in this neighborhood was transformed into ashes and death. One-third of the city was destroyed, 74,800 people were killed and more than 75,000 wounded, At one time, it was said that this area would remain barren for 75 years."

Just to the right of the monument is a huge chunk of brick wall, part of the old Urakami Cathedral, flanked by a stone statue of a saint with no head. To the right of that is the wreckage of one of the iron-bell church towers, twisted into a tangled mass of metal as though a giant had smashed an unwanted toy in a fit of rage. There is another plaque in front of these grim reminders which reads:

The original Cathedral was completed in 1913 after 30 years of voluntary labor service and contributions by Cathuric [*sic*] believers. This wall relic is part of the remains of the southern wall. Notice the stone column slipped out of place by the atomic blast. The stone statue on the column is of our Savior of—

Nagasaki City

You stand in the middle of this plot of ground and look around you. To the west there are houses and shops, a large international sports palace, the new Shiroyama Primary School, and on a prominent hill the new Chinzei Junior High School. To the north there are more houses, a hotel, a bank, and a gaudy, neon-lit Chinese restaurant. To the south, toward downtown Nagasaki, it is even more populated with a row of Western-looking apartment buildings intruding against the sky. All of these structures have one basic thing in common: Every single one of them is no more than twenty-three years old. Everything in sight *had* to be reconstructed from total devastation.

You stand in the middle of the commemorative plot of ground and look eastward—toward the rising sun—and you see the new Urakami Cathedral, where the statues of various saints still stand—shattered, headless, blackened. Several blocks away, overlooking the stone edifice, is the "Glover House," the legendary place where Cho-cho-san supposedly awaited the return of Lieutenant Pinkerton in Puccini's opera *Madame Butterfly*.

The new cathedral is framed against a dramatic background. Rising on the eastern edge of the Urakami Valley is Mt. Kompira, 1,100 feet high and shaped like a clenched fist thrust toward the low-flying clouds which usually hover menacingly over it. The top third of the mountain consists of rocks, gullies, and trees—pines, bamboos, and cedars. Then houses begin to appear, singly at first, then with increasing frequency as your eyes flit down the slopes. And always, on this hillside as on all others in Japan, are the graded-level gardens spread equally and symmetrically across the face of the mountain, neat notches in the earth's hide, "stepping stones to Heaven," a Japanese poet once called them. And at the foot of Mt. Kompira, surrounded now by clusters of houses with green, brown, blue, and red roofs, is the new Nagasaki University and Medical College, a cluster of white buildings—600 yards from Ground Zero.

How do the people of Nagasaki feel today about what happened to them on that unforgettable day? One emotion, deep and total and shared by all, is an utter abhorrence of war in any form. They are against the struggle in Vietnam for they think it may lead to nuclear escalation. They shudder when the Arab-Israeli hostility erupts into violent war for fear it may draw the big powers into it. They are afraid of confrontations, threats, and arms races. Above all, they are against any further use of nuclear weapons, and with good reason. For the rest of the world atomic warfare is still only an abstract possibility. For the Nagasakians it is cold reality. They have been through it.

Are they angry or bitter that they were chosen as a target? Some still regard the American leaders as evil for using such "a fiendish weapon." A few blame their own military leaders for deluding them and prolonging the war. Most, however, blame it on the war itself and say that all wars result in newer, more powerful weapons, and in new ways of killing people.

Some people are able to find a positive result in the bombing. One man said: "The bomb dropped on Nagasaki may have served the purpose of writing off all future nuclear wars. We here are somewhat consoled by the fact that we may have sacrificed ourselves for the sake of the entire world." Another felt that Nagasaki was "the labor pains that may have preceded the dawn of true peace." One woman wrote that she prayed constantly that "no one else after the people of Nagasaki be forced to go through the same sort of ordeal at any time or in any place on earth."

To some extent the ordeal is continuing. The incidence of leukemia among those who were within half a mile of the epicenter has been fifty times the national average. Exposure to radiation has caused other debilitating and incapacitating ailments such as cancer of the thyroid, cataracts, anemia, skin disorders, internal organ damage, and premature aging. As of 1966, hundreds of people were still in hospitals as a result of radioactive diseases. Many other hundreds simply refuse to go at all—until their condition is critical. They know that if they go they are risking job and marriage opportunities by announcing the stigma of being A-bomb survivors. If they do go, and a low white-blood-cell count is found, the patient is convinced that he is doomed. Said one: "An atomic-bomb hospital is a cemetery. We know that no medicine can save us. So we would rather stay at home than pass through the gate of death at the hospital." It is not surprising that the number of suicides among A-bomb survivors has soared.

Even those who were not physically injured often suffered emotional traumas. One Nagasaki mother put it this way: "The A-bomb victims may look normal on the surface, but they nurse wounds deep inside which are shortening their hold on life."

Consider the case of Mrs. Eto, who lost husband, mother, brother, and four children that Thursday. Today Mrs. Eto is a handsome, tall, imposing woman with a wide, white smile that can suddenly illuminate her face. She gives the impression of great inner strength and self-confidence. It is misleading. Mrs. Eto has changed greatly since that day of loss. For months she flinched at sudden light or unexpected noise. Always a self-controlled woman, she found herself constantly on the edge of tears, and any talk of the bombing caused her head to throb and dizziness to come with a rush. Even twenty years afterward, in discussing the day's events her face would crumple and the tears would flow. Hers was a loss almost too great to cope with.

While the rest of the world may have forgotten Nagasaki, the people who were there that day remember it well, including those who were six miles up. Chuck Sweeney and the crew of *Bock's Car* today can talk about their mission calmly and unemotionally. They were doing a job like any other soldier, they say, and all this talk about their guilt feelings is just so much hogwash.

One of the most enduring pieces of misinformation has concerned the mental condition of the men who dropped the bombs. Countless people have asked me, "Didn't a few of those guys go off their rockers because of guilt feelings?" The answer, once and for all, is an emphatic *no*. The myth got started and persists today because the pilot of one of the weather planes on the Hiroshima mission, a man by the name of Claude Eatherly, did have some psychiatric problems after the war, and at one time claimed to be the pilot of the strike plane, the man who dropped the first atomic bomb. He later admitted to feelings of great guilt and anguish over "his inhumane act," and this so-called confession was picked up and reprinted in newspapers and magazines all over the world.

The truth is that no one on either mission, with the exception of Eatherly, who was nowhere near Hiroshima when the bomb was dropped there, has suffered overwhelming remorse over what happened twenty-three years ago. A few have regrets and, with the benefit of hindsight, wish that another way of ending World War II could have been found. But most are in agreement that their actions helped shorten the war considerably and thus actually saved many lives—American and Japanese. Also, they point out the obvious but overlooked fact that it was wartime, they were in service, and the vast majority of those in the military do not give the orders, but obey them.

I have talked with almost every man who was aboard

Bock's Car that day and have found them to be normal, friendly, and well-adjusted. Most left service after the war's end and returned to their old jobs or found new ones. Jimmy Van Pelt went to medical school and is now a doctor in California. Kermit Beahan is with NASA and Don Albury with Eastern Air Lines. Fred Olivi works for the water department in Chicago and Abe Spitzer is happy to be back in his hometown, New York City. Jake Beser is with an electronics firm in Baltimore, Pappy Dehart is back in Texas, Ray Gallagher and Ed Buckley are still good friends in Chicago. Lieutenant-Commander Ashworth, a career navy man, is now Vice-Admiral Ashworth, Deputy Commander of the Atlantic Fleet.

As for Chuck Sweeney, whom I got to know very well indeed, he is still an exuberant, outgoing Irishman. He now wears two hats—one as co-owner of his own leather company in Boston, the other as Brigadier-General Charles W. Sweeney, Deputy Commander of the Massachusetts Air National Guard. As the former command pilot of the Nagasaki mission, Chuck Sweeney is often called upon as a guest speaker. One of his favorite stories is recounting the fears he and the other crew members had after the flight about whether their nearness to the radioactive cloud had affected their reproductive organs. He doesn't think so now, says Sweeney, always with a straight face. You see, Dorothy and Chuck Sweeney have eleven children.

Although the crew is definitely not guilt-wracked, they certainly will never forget their part in history. As each man began to tell me about the mission, I could almost see that epic flight spring into focus in his imagination as if it had been only a few weeks ago instead of over two decades. That mission is etched in each man's mind, and perhaps that accounts for the one trait they have most strongly in common: Today, they are all deeply religious men.

Nor have the people of Nagasaki forgotten. How could they, when they are still suffering and dying? Typical are

Lieutenant Komatsu, his copilot, and crew member, probably the only men ever to fly through the mushroom cloud of an atomic bomb. Chief Petty Officer Umeda was hospitalized immediately after that flight and remained in bed until his death from leukemia two years later. Copilot Tomimura died in 1964, also of leukemia. And today, Lieutenant Komatsu still suffers from anemia, fainting spells, and a periodic low white-blood-cell count.

Then there is Sumako Fukuda, who did not want to go to work that day. Today, Miss Fukuda is a slight, frail woman of 45 with short, black hair. Her face is scarred, patched with red welts, with a stitched swollen lip. Her eyes, pain-filled for years, are now able to meet other eyes without shame about her appearance. Often she wears a long-sleeved sweater and slacks—even in the hottest part of summer—to cover her scarred and burned arms and legs. She doesn't have to worry about perspiration; most of her sweat glands were destroyed. She wears this costume, she says, because "A Japanese woman should not offend people with such ugliness." Sumako Fukuda has become one of Japan's foremost poetesses. Her collection of poems *The Atomic Desert* is one of the most moving accounts of that Thursday in August.

Others have resumed the daily business of living—but with a difference. Reporter Sato is still a newspaperman, but he now sees things and writes with a sensitivity he never had before. Mr. Nishioka, the man who survived both bombs, eventually became Nagasaki Prefectural Governor. Dr. Sakurai married his Nurse Ozaki and is today head of the rebuilt First Branch Hospital. Little Koichi no longer dives for bells in the Urakami River; it would not be appropriate for a 34-year-old businessman. Mr. Nakamura remained with Mitsubishi Industries and still remembers a girl named Summer.

Mr. and Mrs. Honda, both Nagasaki survivors, confront a major problem of many—the fear and superstition of their own countrymen. Today, they are gravely concerned over whether their two children, as "carriers of the A-bomb disease," will be able to marry or to find decent jobs. Although there have been a few cases of children with microencephaly (small brains) who are mentally retarded, studies by both Japanese and American scientists have turned up no evidence to suggest that the atomic bomb affected the growth or the genes of children. Yet many Japanese still believe that there is an "A-bomb disease" and that it is communicable and inheritable.

Today, the citizens of Nagasaki want no favors, no special benefits, other than *not* being regarded as pariahs. They simply want the world to know that they possessed enough *kungeki* (fresh inspiration) to rebuild their devastated city into a dwelling place of peace. *They* remember what happened, and that is enough for them. And they commemorate it in their own special way.

Each August 9, at precisely 11:02, bells ring, sirens sound in the harbor, and all work comes to a halt for a moment of prayer. At the tenth anniversary, over 3,000 people gathered in front of the "Prayer for Peace" statue while hundreds of schoolchildren orphaned by the bomb each released a white dove. It was ten years to the second after the explosion.

That night in an impressive Buddhist ritual, a solemn procession made its way through the valley to the accompaniment of brilliant fireworks, clanging cymbals, and the doleful beat of drums. There were hundreds of children, walking two by two, each pair bearing a tiny raft on which had been set eight paper lanterns aglow with candles. When they reached the Urakami River, the rafts were launched, then pulled downstream by small boats, while a Buddhist dirge was slowly intoned. People thronged the banks and bridges to watch the thousands of lanterns as they floated out to sea. The belief is that the souls of the dead return to earth on the anniversary of their dying. The lanterns lighted their way back to the Eternal.

Bibliography

BOOKS

Albury, Donald, and Van Pelt, James, an unpublished account of the Nagasaki mission.

Akisuki, Tatsuichiro, *Nagasaki Gembakuki*. Tokyo, Akio Watanabe, 1966.

Butow, Robert J. C., *Japan's Decision to Surrender*. Stanford, Calif., Stanford University Press, 1954.

Byrnes, James F., *Speaking Frankly*. New York, Harper & Brothers, 1947.

Craig, William, *The Fall of Japan*. New York, The Dial Press, 1967.

Craven, W. F., and Cate, J. L., Eds., *The Army Air Forces in World War II*, Vol. 5, *The Pacific-Matterhorn to Nagasaki*. Chicago, The University of Chicago Press, 1953.

Feis, Herbert, *Japan Subdued, The Atomic Bomb and the End of the War in the Pacific*. Princeton, N. J., Princeton University Press, 1961.

Giovannitti, Len, and Freed, Fred, *The Decision to Drop the Bomb*. New York, Coward-McCann, Inc., 1965.

Groueff, Stephane, *Manhattan Project: The Untold Story of the Making of the Atomic Bomb*. Boston, Little, Brown and Company, 1967.

Groves, Leslie R., *Now It Can Be Told*. New York, Harper & Brothers, 1962.

Hersey, John, *Hiroshima*. New York, Alfred A. Knopf, 1946.

Hewlett, Richard, and Anderson, Oscar E., Jr., *The New World, 1939–1946.* University Park, Pa., Pennsylvania State University Press, 1962.

Huie, William Bradford, *The Hiroshima Pilot.* New York, G. P. Putnam's Sons, 1964.

Jungk, Robert, *Brighter Than a Thousand Suns.* New York, Harcourt, Brace & World, Inc., 1958.

Kase, Toshikazu, *Journey to the Missouri.* New Haven, Yale University Press, 1950.

Kato, Masuo, *The Lost War.* New York, Alfred A. Knopf, 1946.

Knebel, Fletcher, and Bailey, Charles W., *No High Ground.* Harper & Brothers, 1960.

Lamont, Lansing, *Day of Trinity.* New York, Atheneum Publishers, 1965.

Lifton, Robert Jay, *Death in Life.* New York, Random House, 1967.

Miller, Merle, and Spitzer, Abe, *We Dropped the A-Bomb.* New York, Crowell & Co., 1946.

Nagai, Takashi, *We of Nagasaki.* New York, Duell, Sloan and Pearce, 1951.

Nishida, Kazuo, *Storied Cities of Japan.* Tokyo, John Weatherhill, Inc., 1963.

Osada, Dr. Arata (Compiler), *Children of the A-Bomb.* Tokyo, Uchida Rokakuho Publishing House, 1959.

Ossip, Jerome J., Ed., *509th Pictorial Album,* written and published by the members of the 509th Composite Group, 20th Air Force. Marianas Islands, Tinian, 1945.

Sakomizu, Hisatsune, *Kikanjuka No Shusho Kantei.* Tokyo, Kobun Sha, 1964.

Shohno, Naomi, Ed., in collaboration with Yukio Fujimoto and Fukashi Nakamura, *Actual Facts of the A-Bomb Disaster,* pamphlet published by Hiroshima-Nagasaki World Peace Mission. Hiroshima, 1964.

Togo, Shigenori, *The Cause of Japan.* New York, Simon and Schuster, 1956.

Toyoda, Soemu, *Saigo No Teikoku Kaigun.* Tokyo, Sekai No Nihon Sha, 1950.

Truman, Harry S., *Memoirs,* Vol. 1, *Year of Decisions.* Garden City, New York, Doubleday & Co., Inc., 1955.

Trumbull, Robert, *Nine Who Survived Hiroshima and Nagasaki.* New York, E. P. Dutton & Co., 1957.

U. S. Strategic Bombing Survey, *Reports, Pacific War.* Washington, 1945–1947, Government Printing Office.

No. 2—*Japan's Struggle to End the War*

No. 3—*The Effects of Atomic Bombs on Hiroshima and Nagasaki*
No. 13—*The Effects of Atomic Bombs on Health and Medical Services in Hiroshima and Nagasaki*
No. 46—*The Effects of the Atomic Bomb on Insect and Plant Life in Nagasaki*
No. 94—*Effects of the Atomic Bomb on Nagasaki, Japan*

Williams, Harold S., *Shades of the Past: Indiscreet Tales of Japan.* Tokyo, Charles E. Tuttle Company, 1959.

———, *Tales of Foreign Settlements in Japan.* Tokyo, Charles E. Tuttle Company, 1958.

MAGAZINES AND NEWSPAPERS

Articles in *Look, Newsweek, U.S. News & World Report, Bungei Shunju, The New York Times, Washington Star, Chicago Sun-Times, Washington Post,* New York *Mirror, Asahi Shimbun.*

About the Author

Frank W. Chinnock was born in New York in 1927 and did his undergraduate and graduate work in Princeton, Boston, Cincinnati, and Bloomington, Indiana. After a stint of free-lance writing, he put in a three-year hitch in the Army (Intelligence) in Germany. After the service, he returned to writing until he joined the staff of the *Reader's Digest,* where he was an editor for twelve years. In late 1966, he started work on a project that had long interested him. The result—some two years, 50,000 miles, and hundreds of interviews later—was *Nagasaki: The Forgotten Bomb.* Mr. Chinnock lives in Katonah, N. Y., with his wife and four children.